basic
MICROWAVES

basic
MICROWAVES

Bernard Berkowitz

HAYDEN BOOK COMPANY, INC., NEW YORK

Library of Congress Catalog Card Number 65-16814

Printed in the United States of America

PREFACE

It has rightly been said that no really worthwhile body of knowledge is acquired without effort. However, not all effort is equally productive. In gaining familiarity with a new field of learning, it is often most productive to survey the field in breadth first. This type of observation should certainly be fruitful for those who do not wish to specialize in the field. It likewise will apply to those who wish to delve deeply into the field at a later time without sacrifice of perspective.

This text has been prepared to satisfy the need for a broad introduction to the principles of microwaves. In order not to exclude from its readers those who lack higher mathematical training, use of the calculus is avoided. However, a knowledge of algebra and trigonometry is assumed. Where necessary, a few mathematical aids—vectors and exponentials—are introduced and explained.

Many texts on microwaves commence with a discussion of the theory of transmission lines or of Maxwell's equations. However, starting with either of these time-honored building blocks presumes a prior sophisticated level of understanding on the part of the student. This book makes no such presumption and therefore approaches the subject differently.

Wave phenomena are familiar to all. Consequently, this text commences by presenting conceptual relationships concerning electromagnetic waves in boundless space. After emplanting these concepts, it proceeds to consider the influence of semi-infinite material bodies on electromagnetic waves. Reflection, refraction, and diffraction are described. Antennas that bear a close resemblance to ordinary optical lenses and mirrors are treated. At this juncture, the student will have developed a physical intuition about electromagnetic behavior.

Since the concepts of transmission line theory will now be meaningful, this subject is introduced next. The effects of obstacles and apertures in waveguides are then explained, and the text concludes with a discussion of microwave components.

All photographs are courtesy of Sperry Gyroscope Co.

Bernard Berkowitz

CONTENTS

WAVES IN FREE SPACE

1. The microwave spectrum

For every optical lens or mirror system, a microwave counterpart can be found. Sometimes it is even possible to use one and the same lens or reflector to focus both light and microwave energy. This should not be surprising, since light and microwave energy are completely alike in kind, differing only in frequency. Both are examples of electromagnetic waves. Microwaves occupy a portion of the frequency spectrum (spread of frequencies) between about 0.20 to 300 thousand megacycles per second, whereas light frequencies range from about 400 (red) to 800 (violet) *million* megacycles per second.

A very simple relationship connects the wavelength, frequency, and velocity in a vacuum of all electromagnetic waves, whether they be light waves, X-rays, gamma rays, or just microwaves. If we use the symbols, λ = wavelength, f = frequency, and c = velocity, then we have

$$\lambda = c/f \tag{1.1}$$

The velocity of electromagnetic waves (usually referred to more simply as the velocity of light) in a vacuum is a constant, the value of which is very nearly 30,000 million centimeters per second. If we substitute the microwave frequency limits given above into Eq. 1.1, we find that microwave wavelengths range between

$$\frac{30{,}000 \text{ million cm per sec}}{300{,}000 \text{ million per sec}} = 0.1 \text{ cm}$$

and

$$\frac{30{,}000 \text{ million cm per sec}}{200 \text{ million per sec}} = 150 \text{ cm}$$

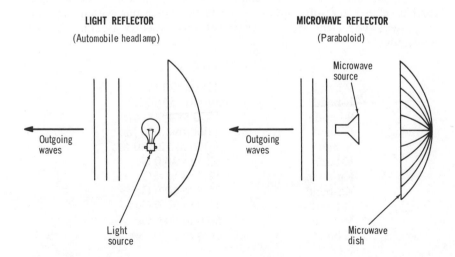

LIGHT REFLECTOR
(Automobile headlamp)

MICROWAVE REFLECTOR
(Paraboloid)

Microwave source

Outgoing waves

Outgoing waves

Light source

Microwave dish

2. Spectral bands and radar bands

Letter abbreviations are utilized by the initiated to designate various portions of the electromagnetic spectrum. In order to expose this alphabet masquerade, we furnish the following tables. We also adopt the common abbreviations for kilocycles (thousands of cycles) per second, kc; mega-cycles (millions of cycles) per second, Mc; and gigacycles (thousands of millions of cycles) per second, Gc.

SPECTRAL BANDS

ELF	Extremely low frequencies	0 to	3 kc
VLF	Very low frequencies	3 to	30 kc
LF	Low frequencies	30 to	300 kc
MF	Medium frequencies	300 to	3000 kc
HF	High frequencies	3 to	30 Mc
VHF	Very high frequencies	30 to	300 Mc
UHF	Ultra high frequencies	300 to	3000 Mc
SHF	Super high frequencies	3 to	30 Gc
EHF	Extremely high frequencies	30 to	300 Gc

Radar usage further subdivides spectral bands into radar bands, as listed below. The original purpose in choosing these letter designations was to obscure their numerical significance to the uninitiated for security reasons during World War II. This purpose seems to have been well served, for even today there is a lack of agreement among authorities as to what frequency ranges the bands constitute. The values below may therefore be taken only as approximate. Some authors neglect to include the C-band, including it as part of the S-band. Some of them, moreover, separate the S- and X-bands at 5200 Mc.

At one time, each of the major bands designated by a capital letter carried small letter subscripts to indicate finer divisions within the band. In present usage, the only survivors of this practice are the Ka- and Ku-bands.

RADAR BANDS

P-band	225 to 390 Mc
L-band	390 to 1550 Mc
S-band	1550 to 4,000 Mc
C-band	4,000 to 8,000 Mc
X-band	8,000 to 12,500 Mc
K-band	12.5 to 40.0 Gc
Ku-band	12.5 to 18.0 Gc
Ka-band	26.5 to 40.0 Gc
Q-band	40.0 to 50.0 Gc
V-band	50.0 to 60.0 Gc
E-band	60.0 to 90.0 Gc

3. The wave concept

The wave concept is fundamental to an understanding of microwaves. In nature there exist only two types of wave motion—longitudinal and transverse. Longitudinal wave vibrations occur parallel to, and transverse wave vibrations perpendicular to, the direction of wave motion. Sound waves are primarily longitudinal; water waves and electromagnetic waves are primarily transverse.

If either of these wave types propagates (moves) without encountering any disturbance, it is known as a traveling wave. However, if the wave strikes an obstacle and is totally or partially reflected back upon itself, an interference pattern or standing wave is formed.

Imagine a person holding taut a rope the opposite end of which is attached to a rigid wall. If suddenly at time t_0 he moves his arms upward and downward repeatedly, he will generate a transverse traveling wave. A short time later, at t_1, the wave will have traveled along the rope to the dotted position in the drawing. The wave will continue to travel until it strikes the wall, when it will be reflected back. If the person ceases his arm movements as soon as the wave strikes the wall, no standing wave will be formed—despite the reflection—because there is no oncoming wave with which the original wave can interfere.

If, on the other hand, the person continues to move his arms at a constant frequency, by the time the leading edge of the wave reflects back to him, a standing wave pattern will have been fully established. Notice in the figure that at periodic intervals along its length the rope does not move at all. These points are known as nodes. In between nodes, each point of the rope oscillates between amplitudes that are constant for that point on the rope but that increase in a sinusoidal fashion to a peak value at a position exactly half way between nodes.

TRANSVERSE WAVES

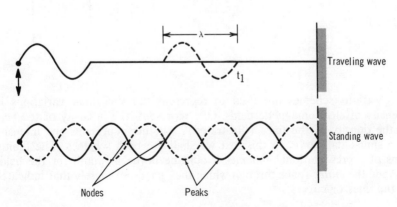

4. Nature of an electromagnetic wave

As its name implies, an electromagnetic wave has associated with it both electric and magnetic fields. Moreover, both exist simultaneously in such a wave; one does not exist without the other. For any given medium in which an electromagnetic wave is propagating, if the electric field is completely known, there is only one magnetic configuration that can accompany it. In other words, the electric and magnetic field relationships are unique in any given medium. In dealing with electromagnetic waves, therefore, it is common to treat only the electric or only the magnetic field, the one selected being merely a matter of convenience.

We have stated that most electromagnetic waves are transverse, that is, either the electric field (E), the magnetic field (H), or both vibrate in a plane perpendicular to the direction of propagation. Both fields are transverse if the electromagnetic waves are traveling far from their source in regions of unobstructed (free) space. Under these circumstances, the simplest of spatial relationships exists between the two fields. We shall therefore consider waves of this type first.

WAVE IN FREE SPACE

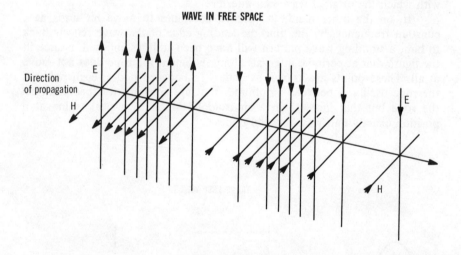

Various schemes are used to represent the sinusoidal variations in intensity of electromagnetic fields. One represents the intensity of the field by the density of the lines (illustrated). Another represents the intensity by a sinusoidal curve. In this text we shall use both schemes. The limitations of representational schemes should be borne in mind, for the fields pervade the *entire* space through which they pass, not merely that indicated by the lines or curves.

5. Electromagnetic wave representation

Consider a transverse electromagnetic (TEM) wave, propagating in free space at velocity c. The figure below is a snapshot representation of the electric field intensity (E) at one instant of time. At another instant, $1/f$ seconds later, the *entire* wave will have moved (say to the right) by a distance exactly equal to one wavelength. An observer located at point A (with an apparatus to measure the instantaneous value of the E field) will note a sinusoidal variation of field intensity with time. An observer at point C will also note a sinusoidal variation. There will be a difference, however, because each is sampling the E field at a different *phase*. Phase defines electrical length in degrees along the wave path. As shown in the figure, it varies linearly at a slope of 360° per wavelength.

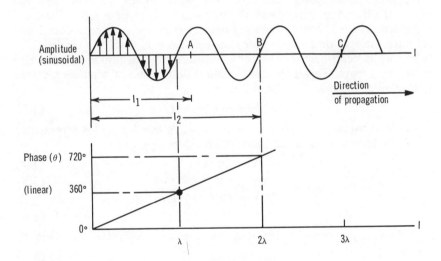

Observers measuring the fields at points B and C will find that they rise and fall precisely in synchronism, as they do at all points separated by distances an exact multiple of a wavelength. Let θ be the phase at any distance l from the origin and ϕ be the phase of point B with respect to point A (the phase separation). We have:

$$\theta = 360\, l/\lambda \text{ degrees} = 2\pi l/\lambda \text{ radians}$$

and

$$\phi = 360°\, (l_2 - l_1)/\lambda \text{ degrees}$$

Notice that the direction in which the E field points (its *sense*) reverses each half wavelength. When two or more waves cross paths, their E fields reinforce one another (interfere constructively) if the fields point in the same direction but diminish one another (interfere destructively) if they are opposed.

6. Mathematical representation

Let an electromagnetic wave be represented by

$$A \sin \omega \, (t - l/c) \qquad (1.2)$$

where

A = peak amplitude of wave

$\omega = 2\pi \times$ frequency of wave, or $2\pi f$

l = distance along propagation path

c = velocity of light

t = time

At any fixed instant of time ($t =$ constant), the wave varies sinu-soidally with distance. Similarly, at any fixed position ($l =$ constant), the wave varies sinusoidally with time. The wave travels outward from the origin at velocity c, and covers the distance to l_0 in time l_0/c. Thus, the waveform which appears near the origin at any time t_0 is reproduced and repeated later at time ($t_0 + l_0/c$) at a distance l_0 from the origin. Such behavior, as described above, really constitutes the definition of what one means by a wave. This is the mathematical description of what we pictured in Section 5. Since $\lambda = c/f$ and $f = c/\lambda$,

$$\omega t = 2\pi f t = (2\pi/\lambda)(ct) \qquad (1.3)$$

The constant, $2\pi/\lambda$, is known as the *wave number* and is represented by k. We therefore have the following relationships:

$$k = 2\pi/\lambda \qquad (1.4)$$
$$\omega t = kct \qquad (1.5)$$
$$\omega(l/c) = (2\pi c/\lambda)(l/c)$$
$$= kl \qquad (1.6)$$

Substituting these in Eq. 1.2, we can now represent the wave by

$$A \sin k(ct - l) \qquad (1.7)$$

Frequently the variation in time is taken for granted, and only the variation with space is of interest. In this event, the wave is simply repre-sented by either of the following

$$A \sin (kl) \qquad (1.8A)$$
$$A \cos (kl) \qquad (1.8B)$$

whichever is appropriate. Both of these equations represent a sinusoidal wave. However, they differ by 90 electrical degrees in the starting phase of the wave. To accommodate a starting phase of any arbitrary value at some reference position, l_1, the initial phase may be taken into account, in which case the two equations become, respectively

$$A \sin (kl + \phi_1) \qquad (1.9A)$$
$$A \cos (kl + \phi_1') \qquad (1.9B)$$

Obviously ϕ_1 and ϕ_1' differ from one another by 90 degrees.

7. Relationship of *E* and *H* fields

The preceding descriptions of the *E* fields of a TEM wave propagating in free space apply as well to the *H* fields. Their behavior in free space (though not necessarily elsewhere, as we shall later find) is very similar, except for spatial orientation. In a TEM wave, the *E* and *H* fields are always perpendicular to one another, and both are perpendicular to the direction of propagation. These relationships are shown in the figure below. When the *E* vector changes sense (direction), so does the *H*.

PLANE POLARIZED TEM WAVE

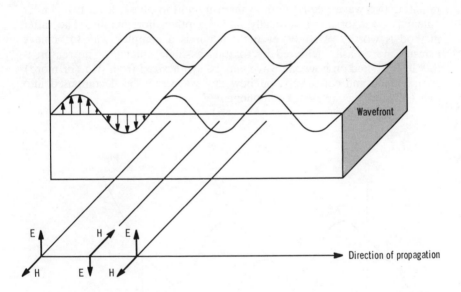

A very simple test suffices to check whether the *E* and *H* vectors are drawn with the proper relative sense. If the *E* vector were to be rotated (about the propagation direction as axis) toward the *H* vector through the smaller of the two possible angles, and if a right-handed screw rotated the same way would progress in the direction of propagation, then the two vectors have the proper relative sense.

In the foregoing we have tacitly assumed the TEM wave to be plane polarized, that is, we have assumed that all *E* vectors are parallel to one another. This is not always the case. Whether it is or not depends both upon the source which launched it and upon the media through which it passes. In dealing with microwaves, we shall have frequent occasion to deal with plane polarized waves.

8. Plane polarized waves

Plane polarized waves are also commonly referred to as linearly polarized waves. Linearly polarized waves are those whose E vector lies entirely in a fixed plane as the wave propagates. The E plane of such waves is that which includes both the E vector and the direction of propagation. Similarly, the H plane contains both the H vector and the direction of propagation. The wavefront, however, is perpendicular to the direction of propagation and therefore includes both the E and H vectors.

Of course, the plane of the E vector may be arbitrarily oriented about the axis (direction) of propagation. However, microwave antennas are usually oriented so as to launch either horizontal or vertical polarization. Occasionally one finds a design in which the E plane is inclined by 45° from the vertical. Alternatively, the 45° inclination may be achieved by radiating two waves, equal both in intensity and in phase, from two similar antennas—one oriented vertically and the other horizontally. The latter method is worthy of study, even though it is a complex way to achieve a result more easily achieved by rotating a single antenna. The reason is that light is shed on how one wave may be synthesized from two (or more) components; and conversely, on how any wave may be decomposed into two (or more) equivalent components.[1]

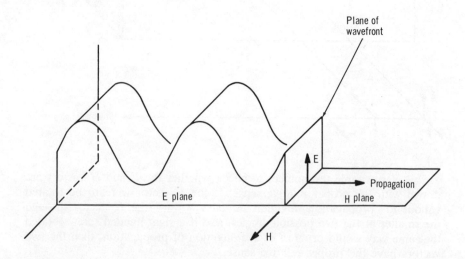

[1] This synthesis and decomposition is often convenient when solving boundary value problems, as when an electromagnetic wave is incident upon an obstacle at some oblique angle. The wave may conveniently be decomposed into normal and parallel components, the problem then solved for each component, and the net resultant synthesized by recombination of the components.

9. Composition of fields

As stated before, when two or more waves cross paths, their E fields reinforce one another (interfere constructively) if the fields point in the same direction but diminish one another (interfere destructively) if they are opposed. Two linearly polarized waves—one vertically (E_v) and the other horizontally (E_h)—that are of the same frequency, magnitude, and phase are indistinguishable in their net effect from a single linearly polarized wave of the same frequency and phase lying entirely in a plane inclined by 45 deg to either. What we have just stated in words, we show pictorially below.

The magnitudes of E_v and E_h are equal at all instants of time (by definition), including, of course, their peak values. It is usual to specify the magnitude of a sinusoidally varying wave by its peak value. In the figure we have arbitrarily set the value at $E_v = E_h = 1.0$ volts per meter. The resultant field, E_r, forms the hypotenuse of a right triangle, of which E_v and E_h constitute the other legs. From the Pythagorean theorem, we have

$$E_r{}^2 = E_v{}^2 + E_h{}^2$$
$$= 1^2 + 1^2 = 2$$

Therefore, $E_r = \sqrt{2} = 1.414$ volts per meter.

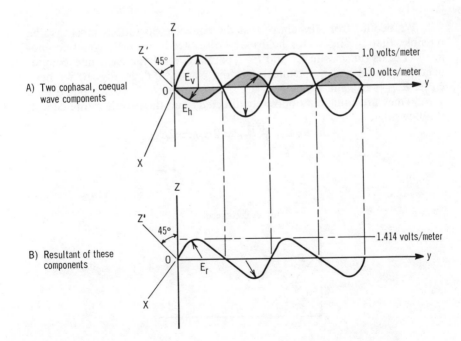

A) Two cophasal, coequal wave components

B) Resultant of these components

10. Vector composition of fields

The resultant of any two fields can be found by applying the rules for vector addition. The net effect of two vectors, acting at the same point in space, is found by displacing one (either one) so that it remains parallel to itself but has its tail joined to the arrow tip of the other. The resultant field has the magnitude and direction of the new vector, which is drawn from the point in space where the two vectors originated to the arrow tip of the displaced vector. The resultant of a vertically polarized and a horizontally polarized field, both acting simultaneously at a point, is shown in Fig. A below. This same result can also be written in the notation, $\overline{E}_v + \overline{E}_h = \overline{E}_r$, where the bars denote that vectors having both magnitude and direction are involved.

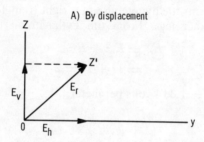

A) By displacement

We deduce from the above that the converse operations must also be possible, that is, any vector field may be resolved into orthogonal components. Let us do so with E_v and E_h separately, resolving each into components tangential and perpendicular to the plane Z'OY. In Fig. B, we have $\overline{E}_h = \overline{E}_{ht} + \overline{E}_{hp}$ and $\overline{E}_v = \overline{E}_{vt} + \overline{E}_{vp}$. Notice that $\overline{E}_{vt} = \overline{E}_{ht}$; but $\overline{E}_{vp} = -\overline{E}_{hp}$ (they are equal but oppositely directed) and the two therefore cancel. It follows that

$$\overline{E}_r = \overline{E}_{vt} + \overline{E}_{ht} = 2\overline{E}_{vt} = 2\overline{E}_{ht}.$$

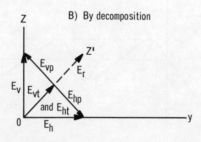

B) By decomposition

11. Circularly polarized waves

An interesting and important composition of two orthogonally polarized waves of equal frequency occurs when both are equal in magnitude but one leads the other by 90° in phase. A circularly polarized wave results. The two components of such a wave are shown in Fig. A. E_r, the resultant of the two components, is shown in Fig. B (as viewed from the origin and looking in the direction of propagation).

$\bar{E}_r$, unchanged in magnitude, constantly rotates about the axis of propagation at the rate of one rotation per cycle of frequency. For the vector relationships shown, right-handed polarization results. The polarization screw sense can be changed to left-handed if the sense of only one (either one) of the two components is reversed. While it sweeps out the circle, the vector $\bar{E}_r$ moves forward at the velocity of propagation. Therefore, its end point really traces out a helix, as shown in Fig. C.

A) Side view   B) End view

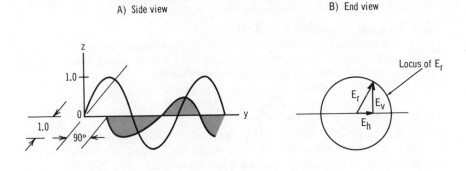

C) Side view of end point

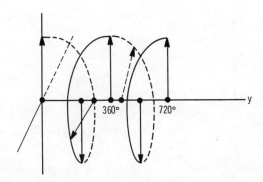

12. Elliptical polarization

Elliptical polarization occurs under the following conditions:

1. If E_v and E_h are in phase quadrature (90° apart) but are *unequal* in magnitude, the terminal point of E_r will trace out an ellipse. The major axis of the polarization will be either vertical or horizontal, respectively, as either E_v or E_h is the larger.

2. If E_v and E_h are unequal, and not in any special phase relationship, we may write

$$y = E_v \cos \theta \text{ and } x = E_h \sin (\theta + \phi) \tag{1.10}$$

where ϕ is any arbitrary phase constant, and $\theta = \omega t$, the variable phase angle. By a little algebraic manipulation and by using the relationships,

$$\sin (\theta + \phi) = \sin \theta \cos \phi + \cos \theta \sin \phi$$

$$\sin \theta = \sqrt{1 - \cos^2 \theta} = \sqrt{1 - (y/E_v)^2}$$

we can arrive at

$$\frac{x^2}{E_h{}^2} - \frac{2xy \sin \phi}{E_v E_h} + \frac{y^2}{E_v{}^2} = \cos^2 \phi \tag{1.11}$$

which is a general equation for an ellipse.

3. An interesting special case of elliptical polarization occurs if E_v and E_h are equal in magnitude but neither cophasal nor in phase quadrature. The value of θ for which E_r is maximized is given by

$$\theta = \frac{90 - \phi}{2} + N \times 180°$$

where N is a positive integer. The figure shows this particular case for $\phi = 45°$. E_r points along the major axis of the ellipse when $\theta = 22.5°$ and $202.5°$; and along the minor axis when $\theta = 112.5°$ and $292.5°$.

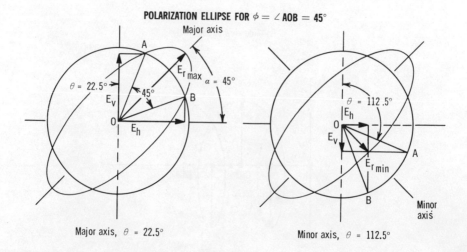

POLARIZATION ELLIPSE FOR $\phi = \angle AOB = $ **45°**

Major axis, $\theta = 22.5°$ Minor axis, $\theta = 112.5°$

13. Elliptical polarization — general case

Let us revert to the general case of elliptical polarization—for which the orthogonal fields are neither equal in magnitude nor in any definite phase relationship—and examine its characteristics. The properties of interest are: (1) the axial ratio, r, of the polarization ellipse; (2) the angle of inclination, α, of the major axis of the ellipse to the horizontal; and (3) the value of the phase angle, θ, for which E_r is maximized. The axial ratio is the ratio of the major to minor axis of the polarization ellipse. Axial ratio is a term now preferred to "ellipticity" since the latter term has been defined in two different ways.[1]

If, as before, $E_v \cos \theta$ and $E_h \sin (\theta + \phi)$ are the two orthogonal components, the following can be derived.

The value of θ for which E_r is maximized is given by

$$\tan 2\theta = \frac{E_h{}^2 \sin 2\phi}{E_v{}^2 - E_h{}^2 \cos 2\phi} \tag{1.12}$$

The inclination α of the major axis is given by

$$\tan 2\alpha = \frac{2 E_v E_h \sin \phi}{E_h{}^2 - E_v{}^2} \tag{1.13}$$

The axial ratio, r, is found from

$$r^2 = \frac{E_v{}^2 \sin^2 \alpha + E_v E_h \sin 2\alpha \sin \phi + E_h{}^2 \cos^2 \alpha}{E_v{}^2 \cos^2 \alpha - E_v E_h \sin 2\alpha \sin \phi + E_h{}^2 \sin^2 \alpha} \tag{1.14}$$

Referring again to the special case discussed in Section 12, we have as given that $E_v = E_h$, and that $\phi = 45°$. These values substituted in Eq. 1.12 determine the value of θ for which E_r is maximized. We get *tan* $2\theta = 1.0$, from which it follows that $\theta = 22.5°$. It should be noted that θ measures the time phase of the E_v component.

The inclination of the major axis is obtained from Eq. 1.13. Substituting in this equation, we have *tan* $2\alpha = \infty$, or $\alpha = 45°$. This angle is indicated in the preceding figure.

Utilizing the fact that $\alpha = 45°$ and substituting in Eq. 1.14, we get $r^2 = (1 + \sin 45°)/(1 - \sin 45°) = 5.83$, from which it follows that r, the axial ratio, is 2.415 and that the ellipticity is 0.414.

Equations 1.12 through 1.14 are applicable to the Lissajous figures traced out when two sine wave generators are connected, one each, to an oscilloscope's vertical and horizontal plates. The correspondence of vertical and horizontal voltage to E_v and E_h, respectively, and of the Lissajous pattern to the elliptical variation of E_r is exact.

---

[1] Ellipticity has been defined as (1) the ratio of the minor to the major axis, and (2) 1.0 minus that ratio.

14. Random polarization

Prior examples have considered electromagnetic fields launched by two "coherent" sources, that is, sources of the same frequency and having a fixed phase relationship. The most general case of polarization occurs when there are many noncoherent sources radiating fields with spatial orientations that are randomly distributed over all possible geometric angles. At a sufficient distance from these sources the net polarization varies in a statistically random fashion. Our sun is a radiator that emits randomly polarized energy over a wide range of the electromagnetic frequency spectrum.

In the microwave art, the push has been toward the development of tunable *coherent* sources of linearly polarized microwave energy—such as klystrons, magnetrons, and more recently, masers and lasers (acronyms standing for *m*icrowave, or *l*ight, *a*mplification by *s*timulation of *e*mission *r*adiation.)

The principal reasons for this push are twofold: (1) Coherent, linearly polarized sources are consistent with (that is, match up with) properties of transmission media known as waveguides, which are designed to rely upon fixed polarizations and fixed phase relationships for their operation. (2) Multiple sources, when coherent and polarized alike, can be combined inside waveguides or in space to achieve vastly greater concentrations of microwave power than is possible with noncoherent sources.

THE KLYSTRON

15. Permeability and dielectric constant

James Clerk Maxwell first derived the mathematical equations that accurately and completely describe the behavior of electromagnetic waves. As a byproduct of Maxwell's equations, the velocity of propagation in space, c, is derived in terms of the dielectric constant, ϵ_0, and permeability, μ_0, of free space:

$$c = 1/\sqrt{\mu_0\epsilon_0} = 3 \times 10^8 \text{ meters/sec} \qquad (1.15)$$

where 10^8 signifies 10 multiplied by itself eight times.

For a medium other than space, the velocity is given by

$$v = 1/\sqrt{\mu\epsilon} \text{ meters/sec} \qquad (1.16)$$

The quantities ϵ and μ are best explained in terms of static electricity and magnetism. The permeability, μ, is the ratio of the flux density, B, produced in a magnetic material when the magnetic field is of strength H:

$$\mu = B/H \qquad (1.17)$$

The dielectric constant, ϵ (also called the specific inductive capacity), has to do with the storage of charge in a medium stressed by an electric field. It is the ratio of the displaced charge density, D, to the electric field strength, E. Thus,

$$\epsilon = D/E \qquad (1.18)$$

Tables of dielectric constants almost always give the *relative* dielectric constant, ϵ_r, that is, the ratio of the material dielectric constant to that of free space (see table below).

Another quantity of interest is the impedance of free space, Z_0. It is the E/H ratio of the wave. From Maxwell's equation it also follows

$$Z_0 = E/H = \sqrt{\mu_0/\epsilon_0} \qquad (1.19)$$

For free space, $Z_0 = 377$ ohms.

TABLE OF RELATIVE DIELECTRIC CONSTANTS

Material	ϵ_r
Styrofoam (depends on density)	1.03 to 1.10
Teflon	2.1
Polyethylene	2.26
Polystyrene	2.5
Plexiglas	2.6
Butyl rubber	2.35
Waxes	2.2 to 2.5
Glass	4.0 to 7.0
Fused quartz	3.8
Titanium dioxide	5.3

16. Power flow

For a short-hand way of stating that the direction of propagation of an electromagnetic wave in free space is perpendicular to the plane containing both $\bar{E}$ and H, and that it advances in the same sense as a right-hand screw, let $\bar{S}$ be a vector in this direction. Then

$$\bar{S} = \bar{E} \times \bar{H} \qquad (1.20)$$

Equation 1.20 is read "E cross H". The vector operator, $\times$, signifies that $\bar{S}$ is orthogonal to the plane containing both $\bar{E}$ and $\bar{H}$. The equation applies at all instants of time, that is, to the instantaneous values of $\bar{E}$ and $\bar{H}$. The magnitude of $\bar{S}$ at any instant yields the power, or the energy flow rate of the electromagnetic wave in the direction of propagation. The usual way to calculate power, however, is to take the time average over an integral number of oscillation cycles.

The value of $\bar{E}$ is generally expressed in volts per meter as a time average. When so expressed, $\bar{S}$ is measured in watts. The time average of $\bar{E}$ is 0.707 times its peak value.

To indicate the magnitude of $\bar{S}$, we write $|\bar{S}|$, or simply S. Its value may be calculated from

$$|\bar{S}| = |\bar{E}| \, |\bar{H}| \sin \theta \qquad (1.21)$$

where θ is the angle between $\bar{E}$ and $\bar{H}$. Equation 1.21 applies generally to any vector quantities. However, in free space, $\bar{E}$ and $\bar{H}$ are everywhere, and at all instants of time, perpendicular to one another. Thus, for free space, $sin\ \theta = sin\ 90° = 1.0$. Furthermore, we have just seen that in free space E and H are related by the impedance, $Z_0 = E/H = 377$ ohms. Substituting this relationship into Eq. 1.21, we now have

$$S = E \times H = E^2/377 \text{ watts per square meter} \qquad (1.22)$$

where E is taken as the time average value in volts per meter.

$\bar{S}$ is known as the Poynting vector, after its discoverer, and appropriately enough, points in the direction of propagation.

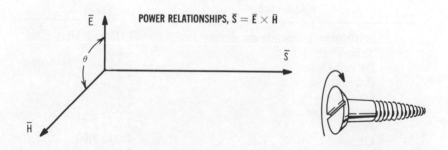

POWER RELATIONSHIPS, $\bar{S} = \bar{E} \times \bar{H}$

17. Power ratios (decibels)

In radio engineering, power levels are commonly given as ratios. These ratios are either referred to some absolute power level or given simply as ratios when the absolute level is of no special significance. The ratio chiefly used is the decibel, abbreviated db. Sometimes a suffix is also appended. For example, when the level referred to is the milliwatt (thousandth of a watt), the abbreviation dbm is used.

If two power levels are p_1 and p_2, their db difference is given by

$$\text{db} = 10 \log (p_1/p_2) = 10 (\log p_1 - \log p_2)$$

where "log" indicates logarithm to the base 10. For example, if $p_1 = 100 = 10^2$, the log of which is 2.0, and $p_2 = 10 = 10^1$, the log of which is 1.0, then

$$\text{db} = 10 \log (100/10) = 10$$

or p_1 is 10 db more than p_2.

If only voltages are expressly known or stated, we have

$$\text{db} = 10 \log (E_1^2/E_2^2)$$

Since $\log E^2 = 2 \log E$, we have

$$\text{db} = 20 \log (E_1/E_2)$$

TABLE OF LOGARITHMS

Voltage ratios		Power ratios		db
V_2/V_1	V_1/V_2	P_2/P_1	P_1/P_2	
1.000	1.000	1.000	1.000	0.00
.891	1.122	.794	1.259	1.00
.794	1.259	.631	1.585	2.00
.708	1.413	.501	1.995	3.00
.631	1.585	.398	2.512	4.00
.562	1.778	.316	3.162	5.00
.501	1.995	.251	3.981	6.00
.447	2.239	.199	5.012	7.00
.398	2.512	.158	6.310	8.00
.355	2.818	.126	7.943	9.00
.316	3.162	.100	10.00	10.00
.282	3.548	.0794	12.59	11.00
.251	3.981	.0631	15.85	12.00
.224	4.467	.0501	19.95	13.00
.199	5.012	.0398	25.12	14.00
.178	5.623	.0316	31.62	15.00
.100	10.00	.0100	100.0	20.00

18. Huygens' principle — wavefronts and rays

In 1690 the Dutch physicist Huygens advanced a concept of how light (electromagnetic) energy propagates. His principle is still valid and useful today. Huygens assumed that every point on the surface of a wavefront constitutes a secondary source from which a hemispherical wave radiates in the general direction of propagation. The surfaces on which these secondary waves are all cophasal (in phase) are what constitute the succeeding wavefronts. In other directions, destructive interference results. As an illustration, consider a few points on a wavefront shown.

Lines in the direction of propagation, perpendicular to successive wavefronts, are known as *rays*. In free space, rays are straight lines (light travels in straight lines). But at interfaces between media, and when electromagnetic energy encounters obstacles, rays bend. These phenomena are called *refraction* and *diffraction*.

Refraction and diffraction are phenomena alike in kind but differing in degree. Both are examples of interference phenomena. By refraction is meant the more or less uniform bending of rays along an interface that leaves the relative intensity of the energy across the wavefront essentially unchanged. Diffraction, on the other hand, occurs when the interface disturbs the original phase and amplitude distribution across the wavefront. In this case, the relative energy distribution is modified by the constructive and destructive interferences from the new sources along the interface. These problems will be considered in the next chapter.

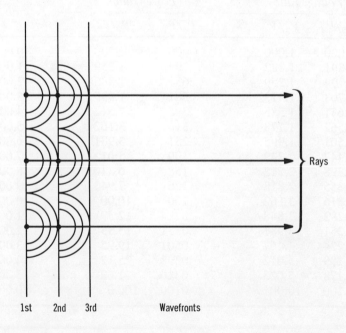

1st   2nd   3rd   Wavefronts

19. Direct and reflected waves

Suppose two coherent electromagnetic waves propagate nearly parallel to one another, crossing at a very shallow angle. As a practical matter, this situation arises when energy from an antenna propagates nearly parallel to the earth's surface, some of its rays' striking the ground and being reflected at a shallow angle. At certain regions above the earth, the direct and reflected rays will interfere constructively (add), and at others, interfere destructively (cancel). The loci of points where rays add or cancel form a nested set of surfaces called *hyperboloids of revolution*. The figure shows the cross section of a few of these surfaces.

For the present purpose it is possible to neglect any phase shift upon reflection of the reflected ray (the concept here described remains valid in any case). With this assumption, addition of rays occurs where the distance, d, from the source to the observation point, P, by the direct path is greater than the reflected ray path, r, by an integral number of wavelengths. That is,

$$d = r + N\lambda \qquad (1.23)$$

Each one of the hyperboloidal surfaces is characterized by one specific value of N. For surfaces where rays subtract, we have

$$d = r + (N \pm 1/2)\lambda \qquad (1.23A)$$

Whenever calculating the power resulting from two or more interfering waves of the same frequency, it is always necessary to perform the vector additions or subtractions using fields.

If, at the observation point P, we let the direct field, E_d, be 1.0 volt/meter and the reflected field, E_r, also be 1.0 volt/meter, the power due to each wave separately is 1/377 watts per sq meter. However, when both are present simultaneously and interfere constructively, the net field is $E_d + E_r = 2.0$ volts/meter. For this case, the resultant average power, S, is

$$S = (E_d + E_r)^2 / Z_0 = 4/377 \text{ watts per sq meter} \qquad (1.24)$$

Had we merely added powers from the two waves separately (2/377 watts/sq meter), we would have arrived at the wrong answer.

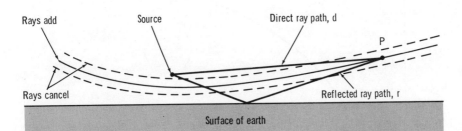

19. Direct and reflected waves (Cont.)

Now, if we move the observation point to a surface where the two rays cancel, and choose the same values of E_d and E_r, we have

$$E_d - E_r = 0.0 \text{ volts} \qquad (1.25)$$

So no energy whatever appears on this surface. If we refer the net power in the two cases above to the power in one wave, we have

$$10 \log 4 = +6.0 \text{ db}$$
$$\text{and} \quad 10 \log 0 = -\infty \text{ db}$$

For in-between cases (field vectors at a phase other than $0°$ or $180°$), the net power in db lies between $+6.0$ db and $-\infty$ db.

In the above examples we have assumed that $E_d = E_r$. Usually, however, E_r is less than E_d. In the abscissa of the graph entitled "Perturbations to Direct Energy," the ratio of E_d to E_r is given as a power ratio, that is, $db = 20 \log E_d/E_r$. The curves represent—as a function of power ratio— peak and minimum values for in-phase and anti-phase conditions, respectively. For in-between cases of phase, the net power lies between the curves.

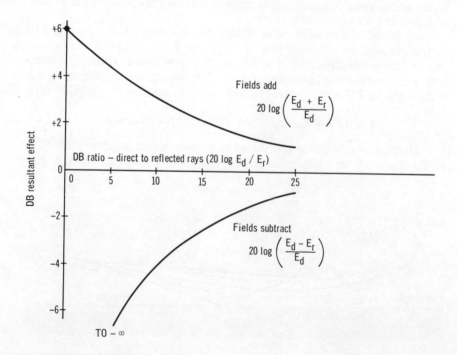

PERTURBATIONS TO DIRECT ENERGY

20. The imaginary exponential

In a preceding section we have seen that, ignoring time variations, *cos kl* and *sin kl* are used to represent linearly polarized waves. A useful extension of this concept is the following. By definition let

$$e^{jkl} = cos\ kl + j\ sin\ kl \tag{1.26}$$

The number, *e*, is the irrational base (2.71828++) and is raised to the exponent, *jkl*. The imaginary constant, *j*, is defined as $\sqrt{-1}$, so that $j^2 = -1$. A simple geometrical meaning of *j* is that it operates so as to rotate a vector by 90°. Hence *cos kl* and *j sin kl* are waves that are orthogonally polarized. The angle, *kl*, is called the *argument* of the trigometric function.

Thus, one use for the exponential, e^{jkl}, is to represent both components of a circularly polarized wave. The *j* operator takes care of the space rotation by 90°, and, of course, sine and cosine functions are 90° apart in phase, since

$$sin\ (\theta + 90°) = cos\ \theta \tag{1.27}$$

Usage of the imaginary exponential as a vector operator must be distinguished from its usage below as a phasor operator. In this sense, it is used to represent the phase of a linearly polarized wave, and what is really understood is the real part (r.p.) of e^{jkl}. Hence,

$$(\text{r.p.})\ e^{jkl} = cos\ kl \tag{1.28}$$

REPRESENTATION OF e^{jkl} AS ROTATING VECTOR

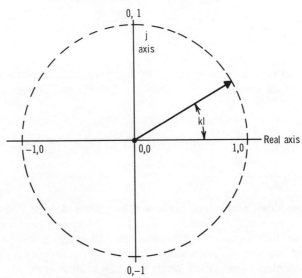

21. Phasor composition

The magnitude of $e^{j\omega t}$ for the argument, $\omega t,$ is always unity. The two components, $cos\ \theta$ and $sin\ \theta,$ form a right triangle; thus, $cos^2\ \theta + sin^2\ \theta = 1$. Therefore, $Ae^{j(\omega_1 t + \phi_1)}$ and $Be^{j(\omega_2 t + \phi_2)}$ represent sinusoidal waves of amplitudes A and $B,$ respectively, angular frequencies ω_1 and $\omega_2,$ and phases ϕ_1 and ϕ_2. If the two waves are of the *same* angular frequency, $\omega_1 = \omega_2 = \omega,$ the two phasors rotate at the same velocity, and the *relative* orientation of the two at all instants of time is fixed and equal to any phase difference at $t = 0$. To find the resultant of two such waves of the same frequency, the rotation can be stopped at any instant of time, and the phasors can be treated like vectors.

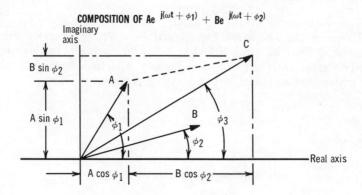

COMPOSITION OF $Ae^{j(\omega t + \phi_1)} + Be^{j(\omega t + \phi_2)}$

We shall now use this concept to determine the resultant of any two sine waves of the same frequency, $Ae^{j\phi_1}$ and $Be^{j\phi_2},$ and phases ϕ_1 and ϕ_2 at time $t = 0$.

The resultant is a single sine wave of magnitude C and phase angle ϕ_3.

$$C = \sqrt{(A\ sin\ \phi_1 + B\ sin\ \phi_2)^2 + (A\ cos\ \phi_1 + B\ cos\ \phi_2)^2} \quad (1.29)$$

$$tan\ \phi_3 = \frac{A\ sin\ \phi_1 + B\ sin\ \phi_2}{A\ cos\ \phi_1 + B\ cos\ \phi_2} \quad (1.30)$$

This resultant sine wave may now be summed with still another to form a new resultant. Obviously, this procedure may be continued indefinitely, so that we may now make the following generalization: *The sum of any number of sinusoidal waves of the same frequency but of arbitrary magnitude and phase angle is a single sine wave.*

Summary of Chapter 1

Electromagnetic waves in free space are transverse waves with coexisting electric and magnetic components. These components are related by the impedance of space, Z_0, defined by $Z_0 = E/H$. The velocity of such waves in free space, c, equals the velocity of light, so that $c = \sqrt{\mu_0/\epsilon_0}$, where μ_0 and ϵ_0 are the permeability and permitivity (dielectric constant) of space, respectively. The phase of electromagnetic waves is directly proportional to propagation distance, and the proportionality constant is known as the wave number.

When the electric vector oscillates in a fixed plane, the wave is said to be linearly polarized. The resultant of two or more linearly polarized waves may be found by vector addition. In general, elliptic polarization occurs, which includes both circular polarization and linear polarization as special cases. Rate and direction of power flow may be determined from the Poynting vector. Relative power is measured in decibels, a useful unit. Another useful expression is the imaginary exponential $e^{j\theta}$, which may represent orthogonal space (vector) components or orthogonal time (phasor) components.

Questions

1. Calculate the wavelength of (a) red and (b) violet light.

2. If a rope is vibrating in a standing wave pattern with a peak amplitude of 1.0 in. and a separation between nodes of 10.0 in., find the amplitude at (a) 2.5 in., (b) 5.0 in., and (c) 7.5 in. from a node.

3. Calculate the phase difference, at 3 Gc/sec, between two points separated by 12 in. along the direction of propagation.

4. Find the wave number for a frequency of (a) 3 kc/sec, (b) 3 Mc/sec, and (c) 3 Gc/sec.

5. Find the resultant inclination of two cophasal, orthogonal waves of the same frequency if $E_v = 2$ volts/meter and $E_h = 1$ volt/meter? Draw the vector diagram solution.

6. Starting from Eq. 1.11 under Elliptical Polarization, derive the simplified equations resulting for the cases of (a) $\phi = 0$, (b) $\phi = 0$ and $E_h = E_v$, and (c) ϕ arbitrary but $E_h = E_v$. Plot the results for a, b, and c, and describe each case.

7. Letting $E_v = 2 E_h$, and $\phi = 30°$, calculate the polarization ellipse characteristics, θ, α, and r. Sketch the ellipse.

8. What is the *magnitude* of the quantity $e^{j\pi/3}$? Sketch the vertical and horizontal components of a circularly polarized wave represented by $e^{j\pi/3}$.

9. Find the resultant of two sine waves whose magnitudes are 1.0 and 3.0 volts/meter, respectively, if their phase difference is (a) 30°, (b) 45°, and (c) 60°.

22. Introduction

Chapter 1 dealt with electromagnetic waves in free space. Detection of such waves requires the introduction of material bodies (antennas, transmission lines, crystals, and the like) upon which the waves can impinge to transfer their energy. It thus becomes necessary to study the properties of electromagnetic energy in the presence of various configurations and types of matter. Certain conditions must be satisfied at material boundaries; the boundaries in turn affect the distribution of electromagnetic fields.

For convenience in studying boundary problems, matter can be treated as if there were three "pure" states: perfect (lossless) conductors, lossless dielectrics, and lossy materials. Actual matter is a hybrid of all three states. However, many common materials have properties that fall predominantly into one category. Metals behave like perfect conductors, plastics and ceramics like lossless dielectrics, and dispersions of carboniferous matter like lossy material.

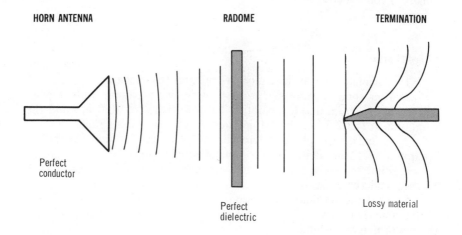

HORN ANTENNA   RADOME   TERMINATION

Perfect
conductor

Perfect
dielectric

Lossy material

Concepts presented in this chapter are essential to a fuller understanding of the operation of any microwave device and will permit a physical insight into its operation. Qualitatively, this is often sufficient. The concept of tubes of force, introduced over a century ago, is retained here because it very effectively permits visualization of the mechanism of radiation (described in the next chapter). For quantitative results, however, it is necessary to develop equations for representing behavior of the electromagnetic waves in bounded media. It is the object of this chapter to present the fundamental physical phenomena which can later be utilized to deduce numerical results.

23. Lines and tubes of force

The concept of using lines—or really, tubes—to represent static electric fields was first employed by Faraday. A knowledge of their properties is helpful. We have already used density—number of lines per unit length or area—to represent field strength. Additional properties may be defined as follows:

1. Tubes terminate on charges. At opposite ends of the same tube, the charges are unlike in sign.
2. Tubes tend to increase their radii; each expands until stopped by the pressure of opposing tubes that are likewise expanding. Magnetic fields surrounding each tube exert these opposing forces.
3. If the charges upon which they terminate disappear, tubes shrink longitudinally, and disappear.

When used to represent time-varying rather than static fields, tubes of force exhibit all the above properties and several additional ones as well:

1. Tubes, forming open loops, can close upon themselves (as well as on charges).
2. Tubes exhibit momentum (this property is useful in explaining how antennas radiate).

When TEM modes propagate through a set of parallel conducting plates, charges of opposite sign appear on the top and bottom plates to terminate the lines. When the propagation is such that the E vector is parallel to the plates, a TE mode (which will be treated shortly) exists, and the magnetic fields surrounding the tubes nearest the plates excite surface currents. These currents create an image of the tube in the plates, thus preventing the tube from touching the plates (E falls to zero).

TEM Mode   TE Mode

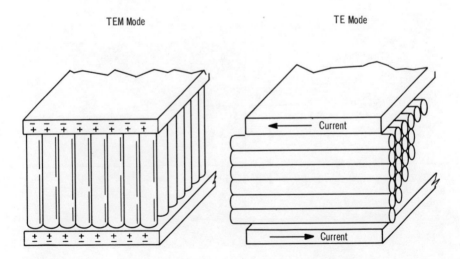

24. Boundary conditions

At interfaces between different media, certain boundary conditions must be satisfied. Their derivation is beyond the scope of this book, but the results can be simply stated and are important to all interface problems. These relationships apply at (an infinitesimal distance from) the surface of separation of the two media.

1. *Tangential* components of E are the same on both sides of the surface.

2. *Normal* components of displacement, $D = \epsilon E$, are equal if there is no charge on the surface. If a surface charge, ρ_s, exists, then $D_2 - D_1 = \rho_s$, that is, some of the D_1 tubes terminate on charges, and the remainder are continuous.

3. *Tangential* components of H differ when surface currents, J_s, and displacement currents, J_D, are excited. Thus, $H_2 - H_1 = J_D + J_s = J$. Displacement currents are generated when the displacement, D, changes as a function of time, just as currents "flow" through a capacitor.

4. *Normal* components of B are the same on both sides of the surface.

In applying these conditions, the incident wave is resolved into transmitted and reflected components. For lossy media, the "transmitted" wave must include the absorbed field as well as that propagated.

At a perfect dielectric interface, no conduction currents flow; the reflected wave is generated entirely by the excitation of displacement currents. In other words, the dielectric electrons are set into oscillation by the oscillating forces of the incident electric field, but are not removed from their atomic location. At a perfect conductor interface, large conduction currents flow, and electrons responding to these forces are displaced large distances. In fact, because of the ease of their flow, no displacement currents can exist.

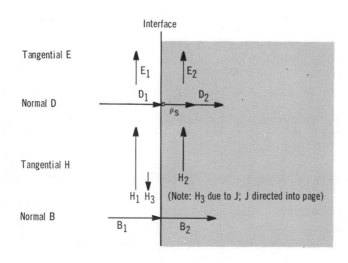

25. Reflections from perfectly conducting surfaces

When electromagnetic waves impinge obliquely upon perfectly conducting, flat surfaces, two special cases are of interest. In both cases, if the incident ray encounters the surface at some incident angle, *i,* with respect to the surface normal, the ray is reflected at an *equal* angle, *r,* on the opposite side of the normal. The two cases are distinguished by the orientation of *E* with respect to the plane containing both the incident ray and the surface normal at the ray's point of contact (the plane of incidence). These cases are (1) *E* is perpendicular to the plane of incidence, that is, $E = E_\perp$, and (2) *E* lies entirely parallel with this plane, that is, $E = E_\parallel$. The first case is simpler to deal with, for $E_\perp$ lies entirely parallel to the surface.

1. E *perpendicular to plane of incidence*—As $E_\perp$ falls on the surface, it excites surface currents of a magnitude that precisely cancels it at the surface. These currents excite a reflected wave that is 180° out of phase with respect to the incident wave at the surface. It is possible to satisfy the boundary conditions of the surface by replacing it with an imaginary (virtual) wave emanating, as shown, from behind the surface. Notice the phase relationships of *H* with respect to *E* before and after reflection. These relationships can be deduced from the fact that the Poynting vector points in the direction of the reflected ray.

E PERPENDICULAR TO PLANE OF INCIDENCE
Frontal view

25. Reflections from perfectly conducting surfaces (Cont.)

2. E *parallel to plane of incidence*—For this case, $E_\parallel$ has components both parallel and perpendicular to the conducting surface. The figure shows a top view of the surface with the E vector, incident ray, and reflected ray all in the plane of incidence.

At the point of reflection, $E_\parallel$ may be resolved into its two components. The perpendicular component induces a charge at the conductor surface upon which the lines of force terminate. There is therefore no change of phase associated with this component upon reflection. The parallel component excites opposing currents in the surface and therefore undergoes a 180° phase change upon reflection. Upon reflection, moreover, parallel and perpendicular components recombine to form a reflected wave that suffers no change in phase *as viewed in the direction of propagation.*[1] Again, the phase of H must be taken so as to satisfy the Poynting direction.

For this case, as well as the previous one, it is possible to satisfy all boundary conditions by replacing the perfectly conducting surface with a virtual wave. We shall shortly utilize this concept.

E PARALLEL TO PLANE OF INCIDENCE
(top view)

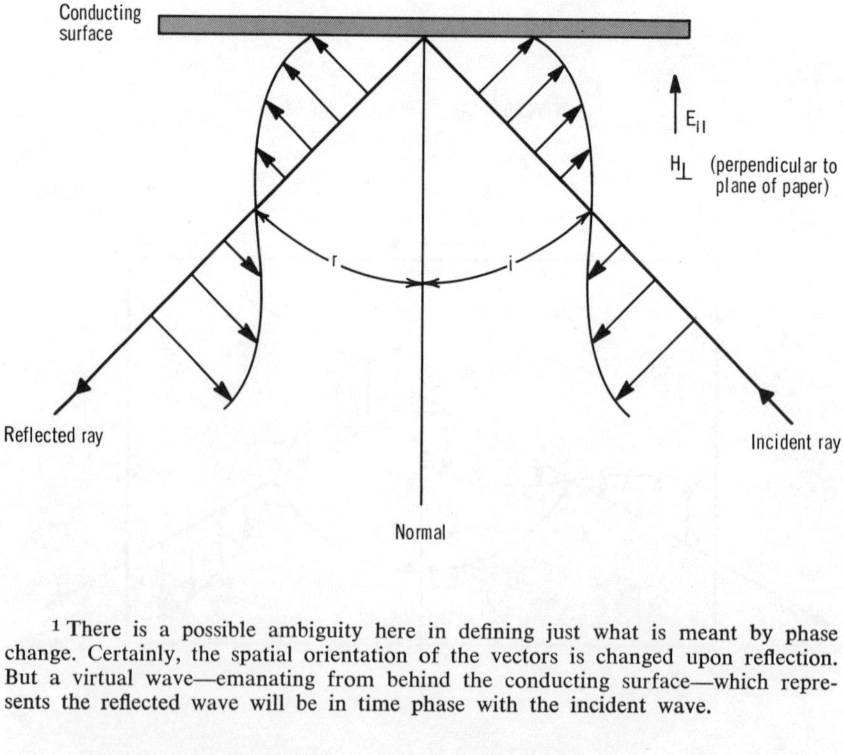

---

[1] There is a possible ambiguity here in defining just what is meant by phase change. Certainly, the spatial orientation of the vectors is changed upon reflection. But a virtual wave—emanating from behind the conducting surface—which represents the reflected wave will be in time phase with the incident wave.

26. Normal incidence reflections from perfect conductors

When wavefronts impinge normally upon planar surfaces, the E vector is parallel to the surface. The angle of incidence and the angle of reflection both equal zero, and the wave is reflected back upon itself. Standing waves are formed that are exactly analogous to the transverse standing waves on a rope incident on a perfectly rigid wall (considered in Chapter 1).

Let e^{jkl} represent a plane wave traveling to the right, and e^{-jkl} a similarly polarized wave of equal amplitude traveling to the left. Furthermore, let a perfectly conductive planar surface be at a distance, L, from the source.

The phase of the source wave at one arbitrary null, position P, is kl. At the same position, the reflected wave has undergone a total phase shift of $k\{L + (L - l)\} + \phi$ since leaving the source. The phase shift on reflection, ϕ, equals π radians for a perfect conductor. Thus,

$$\text{Phase of source wave} = kl = 2\pi l/\lambda \qquad (2.1)$$

$$\text{Phase of reflected wave} = (2\pi/\lambda)(2L - l) + \pi \qquad (2.2)$$

At every null these two phases must differ by an odd number $(2N - 1)$ of half-wavelengths. Therefore, we can write

$$(2\pi/\lambda)(2L - l) + \pi - (2\pi l/\lambda) = (2N - 1)\pi \qquad (2.3)$$

Solving for $(L - l)$, the distance of position P from the surface, we arrive at the fact that nulls are located every half-wavelength from the surface:

$$L - l = (N - 1)(\lambda/2) \qquad (2.4)$$

STANDING WAVE LOCATIONS

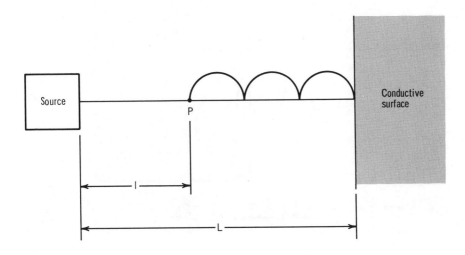

27. Index of refraction

When electromagnetic energy travels through a medium, such as a lossless dielectric, its speed differs from its speed in a vacuum. The ratio of speeds, in-vacuum to in-medium, is called the index of refraction of the medium; it is symbolized by n. Therefore, calling v_m the velocity in the medium,

$$n = c/v_m = \sqrt{\mu\epsilon/\mu_0\epsilon_0} \tag{2.5}$$

We find that the frequency of a wave is not altered as it traverses different media, but its wavelength is, so that the relationship

$$f_m = f = v_m/\lambda_m \tag{2.6}$$

is maintained constant. Since this is so, we can also define n as

$$n = \lambda/\lambda_m \tag{2.7}$$

The latter definition provides a more convenient handle with which to determine n, since it is much easier to measure the wavelength than it is to measure the velocity of an electromagnetic wave.

Most dielectric media are not ferromagnetic. For these media, $\mu = \mu_0$. Also, since ϵ/ϵ_0 is the relative dielectric constant, we may write for such media

$$n = \sqrt{\epsilon/\epsilon_0} = \sqrt{\epsilon_r} \tag{2.8}$$

WAVE AT VACUUM-DIELECTRIC INTERFACE FOR n = 3

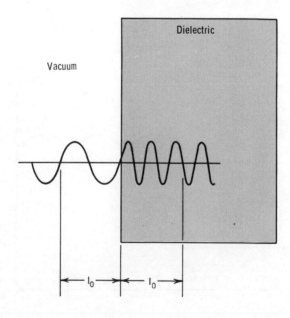

28. Snell's Law

Consider two adjacent, parallel rays, shown in the diagram to be traveling from Medium 1, which for convenience we take as a vacuum, into Medium 2, of greater index of refraction. At time $t = t_1$, one of these rays is just impinging on the dielectric of Medium 2 at point B. At a later time, $t = t_2$, the other ray is just impinging on the dielectric interface. In the time $(t_2 - t_1)$, it has traveled a distance $c(t_2 - t_1) = AC$. In the same time interval, the first ray has traveled only the distance, $v_m(t_2 - t_1) = BD$. The ratio of these distances equals the index of refraction of Medium 2.

$$\frac{AC}{BD} = \frac{c(t_2 - t_1)}{v_m(t_2 - t_1)} = \frac{c}{v_m} = n \qquad (2.9)$$

The angles which the incident and refracted rays make with the normal to the surface are known as the angle of incidence, i, and angle of refraction, r, respectively.

Since $sin\ i = AC/AB$ and $sin\ r = BD/AB$, the ratio of these two is also equal to the index of refraction, for

$$\frac{Sin\ i}{Sin\ r} = \frac{AC/AB}{BD/AB} = \frac{c}{v_m}$$

Thus,

$$n = sin\ i / sin\ r \qquad (2.10)$$

Equation 2.10 is known as Snell's Law (after its discoverer).

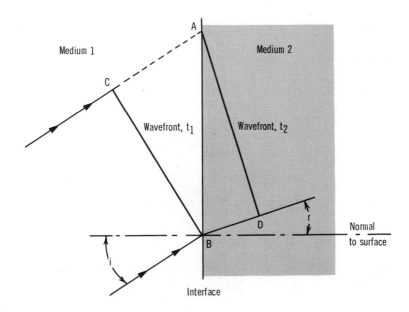

29. Internal reflections

It should be observed in the preceding section that the rays were bent toward the normal after entering Medium 2 of greater *n*. If the rays were traveling in the opposite direction, from Medium 2 to Medium 1, the same diagram would apply; the rays, however, bend away from the normal. Snell's law can *always* be satisfied when rays proceed to a denser medium but not always when they proceed to a less dense medium.

For example, suppose the angle of incidence (*r*, in this case) is chosen large enough so that *n sin r* is greater than 1.0. Obviously, *sin i* cannot exceed 1.0, and there is no solution—no refraction, that is. What happens in this case is that total internal reflection occurs, and the interface behaves just as if it were a mirror.

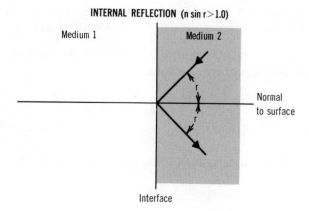

INTERNAL REFLECTION (n sin r > 1.0)

Medium 1

Medium 2

Normal to surface

Interface

Usually (the case just described is an exception), there are three components of a wave at an interface. These are the incident, reflected, and transmitted waves.

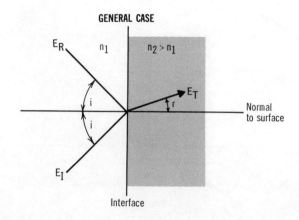

GENERAL CASE

E_R

n_1

$n_2 > n_1$

E_T

Normal to surface

E_I

Interface

30. Fresnel equations for lossless dielectric

1. E *perpendicular to plane of incidence (Case 1)*—Although we have determined relative directions for the incident, reflected, and transmitted rays at a dielectric interface, we have not related their magnitudes. These are provided by the Fresnel equations. Distinctions must be drawn for the two possible planes of polarization, just as was done for reflections from perfect conductors.

For $E_\perp$, perpendicular to the plane of incidence, E is entirely parallel to the interface. Its tangential components on both sides of the boundary must therefore satisfy the continuity condition for tangential E:

$$E_I + E_R = E_T \qquad (2.11)$$

The magnetic field accompanying $E_\perp$ is perpendicular to it and parallel to the plane of incidence. Tangential components of $H_\parallel$ may be equated, since, for our lossless dielectric, no conduction currents flow at the interface. Therefore,

$$H_I \cos i - H_R \cos i = H_T \cos r \qquad (2.12)$$

where i and r are, respectively, the angles of incidence and refraction. Furthermore, since we are not dealing here with a ferromagnetic medium, we can let $\mu_1 = \mu_2 = \mu_0$. Since $E_\perp/H_\parallel = Z = \sqrt{\mu_0/\epsilon}$, we can rewrite Eq. 2.12

$$\sqrt{\epsilon_1/\mu_0}\, E_I - \sqrt{\epsilon_1/\mu_0}\, E_R = \sqrt{\epsilon_2/\mu_0}\, E_T \qquad (2.13)$$

Multiplying both sides of Eq. 2.13 by $\sqrt{\mu_0/\epsilon_1}$, and recalling that $\sqrt{\epsilon_2/\epsilon_1}$ is the relative index of refraction, we get

$$(E_I - E_R) \cos i = n\, E_T \cos r \qquad (2.14)$$

Multiplying both sides of Eq. 2.11 by $\cos i$, we get

$$(E_I + E_R) \cos i = E_T \cos i \qquad (2.15)$$

Adding Eqs. 2.14 and 2.15 together yields

$$\frac{E_T}{E_I} = \frac{2 \cos i}{n \cos r + \cos i} \qquad (2.16)$$

Solving Eq. 2.16 for E_T and substituting in Eq. 2.11, we get

$$\frac{E_R}{E_I} = \frac{\cos i - n \cos r}{n \cos r + \cos i} \qquad (2.17)$$

Equations 2.16 and 2.17 are the desired Fresnel equations.

30. Fresnel equations for lossless dielectric (Cont.)

2. E *parallel to plane of incidence* (*Case 2*)—For this case, H is entirely parallel to the interface. Equating tangential H yields

$$H_I + H_R = H_T \tag{2.18}$$

Tangential components of E may also be equated:

$$E_I \cos i - E_R \cos i = E_T \cos r \tag{2.19}$$

Manipulating Eqs. 2.18 and 2.19 in a fashion similar to that for the previous case, we arrive at the second set of Fresnel equations:

$$\frac{E_T}{E_I} = \frac{2 \cos i}{n \cos i + \cos r} \tag{2.20}$$

and,

$$\frac{E_R}{E_I} = \frac{n \cos i - \cos r}{n \cos i + \cos r} \tag{2.21}$$

Equation 2.21 is of particular interest when $n \cos i = \cos r$, for then the reflected wave amplitude is zero. The incident angle for which this condition occurs is called Brewster's angle. Brewster first noted that incident visible light, if randomly polarized, becomes linearly polarized after reflection from a dielectric at this angle. Reflections are caused solely by $E_\perp$, since $E_\parallel$ is entirely suppressed. By a little trigonometric juggling, and using Snell's Law, it can be shown that Brewster's angle is also given by $\tan i = n$.

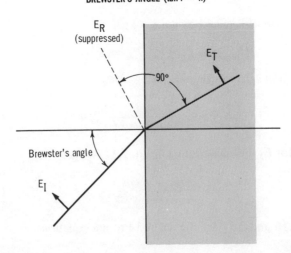

BREWSTER'S ANGLE ($\tan i = n$)

FRESNEL EQUATIONS FOR n = 2.0

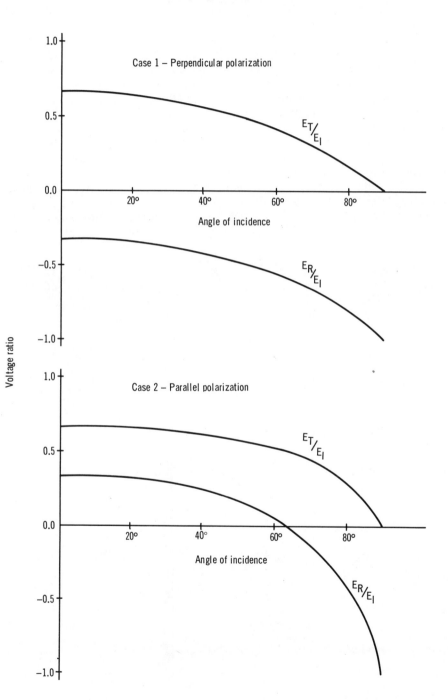

31. Voltage standing wave ratio (VSWR)

If a plane wavefront impinges normally upon a planar surface that is *not* perfectly conductive, standing waves similar to those back of a perfect conductor are formed. However, important differences are found. The phase shift is *not* exactly equal to π radians, and the standing waves do *not* have perfect nulls, merely minima. The kinds of surfaces that we are now considering might be metallic (and have small but finite losses) or slabs of dielectric (and be both transmissive and lossy).

In either case, the incident region near the surface is composed of the sum of a sending wave, a reflected wave, and a transmitted (or absorbed) wave. Only a fractional part of the sending wave interferes with the reflected wave to form a standing wave.

The reflected wave, E_R, will interfere with the sending wave, E_S, forming a (partial) standing wave whose minima do not fall to zero. The voltage delivered to a probe sampling the field to the left of the conductor varies as a function of distance. VSWR is the ratio of maximum to minimum voltage. Therefore,

$$\text{VSWR} = \frac{E_S + E_R}{E_S - E_R} \tag{2.22}$$

The Greek symbol eta, η, is used to designate power standing wave ratio. Since power is proportional to the square of the voltage,

$$\eta = \left(\frac{E_S + E_R}{E_S - E_R} \right)^2 \tag{2.23}$$

REFLECTIONS FROM IMPERFECT SURFACE

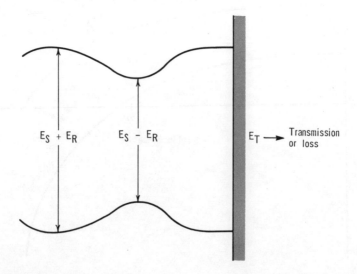

32. Reflection and transmission coefficients

The voltage ratio of the reflected wave to the sending wave is known as the reflection coefficient, ρ.

$$\rho = E_R/E_S \tag{2.24}$$

Substituting this value into Eq. 2.22, we have

$$\text{VSWR} = \frac{1+\rho}{1-\rho} \tag{2.25}$$

Solving for ρ and letting $\sqrt{\eta} = \text{VSWR}$, we have

$$\rho = \frac{\sqrt{\eta}-1}{\sqrt{\eta}+1} \tag{2.26}$$

The quantity, ρ^2, is the fractional power in the reflected wave. A very useful relationship, it is plotted on the next page.

$$\rho^2 = \left(\frac{\sqrt{\eta}-1}{\sqrt{\eta}+1}\right)^2 \tag{2.27}$$

The transmission coefficient, τ, is the ratio of transmitted voltage to sending voltage. Thus,

$$\tau = E_T/E_S \tag{2.28}$$

At a lossless interface, power is conserved. If impedances are equal on both sides of the interface, the sending voltage must equal the *vector* sum of the transmitted and reflected voltages:

$$\overline{E}_S + \overline{E}_R = \overline{E}_T \tag{2.29}$$

or,

$$\overline{1.0} + \overline{\rho} = \overline{\tau} \tag{2.30}$$

VECTOR RELATIONSHIP AT INTERFACE

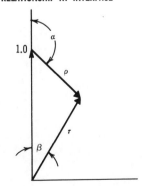

32. Reflection and transmission coefficients (Cont.)

This relationship, for arbitrary values of ρ and τ, is sketched in the drawing, where the phase angle of ρ, α, and of τ, β, are referred to the sending phase.

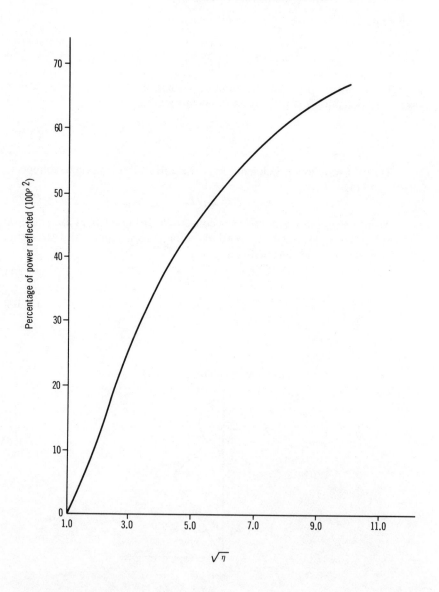

REFLECTED POWER RELATIVE TO VSWR

33. Wave incident on pier

We must confess a failure to distinguish between different kinds of velocities of propagation. Previously there was no need. In unbounded media, the phase velocity—which we shall differentiate from the velocity of energy propagation—usually differs not at all from the ordinary propagation velocity. When it does differ, an interference effect is responsible.

As a common-experience illustration of the concept, consider ocean waves that are incident almost perpendicularly to a pier. A wave crest impinges upon the pier, and the splash "travels" the pier's length at great speed, far exceeding the wave velocity.

To calculate the splash velocity, v_s, one needs to know the wave velocity, v_w, and the angle, ϕ, between the wavefront and the pier. The figure below represents matters when the wavefront first impinges on the near corner of the pier. At that instant, the wave must still travel a distance, s, to reach the far corner of the pier. It does so in time, t.

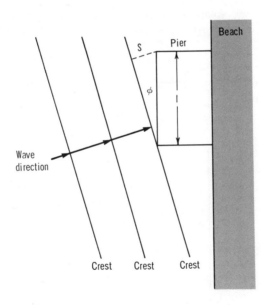

In the same time, t, the splash travels the length, l, of the pier. Since $s/l = sin\ \phi$, we have

$$\sin \phi = s/l = v_w t/v_s t = v_w/v_s \tag{2.31}$$

or

$$v_s = v_w/sin\ \phi \tag{2.32}$$

If $\phi = 0°$, the splash travels at infinite velocity; if $\phi = 90°$, then $v_s = v_w$.

34. Crossing waves

Let us extend the concept of the preceding section to the interference pattern formed when two waves of the same frequency cross. In some arbitrarily chosen interference region, ABCDEF, new wave patterns are formed for which a new phase velocity and new wavelength can be defined.

If the angle formed between the two approaching waves is 2ϕ, the interference wave travels in the direction of their bisector at an angle ϕ with respect to both.

The figure depicts the crests of the waves as solid lines and their extensions in the interference region as dotted lines. As shown, therefore, both waves are in phase at points C and D. At the point, 0, midway between C and D, both waves have their troughs in coincidence. In fact, both waves are everywhere in phase at all points along the line BCD.

Along this line, the interference wavelength, λ_i, exceeds λ, and is given by

$$\lambda_i = \lambda/sin\,\phi \qquad (2.33)$$

Just as for the splash velocity in the preceding example, the phase velocity of the interference wave exceeds the velocity of propagation of energy. Hence

$$v_p = v/sin\,\phi \qquad (2.34)$$

The frequency of the interference wave is identical with that of the two approaching waves.

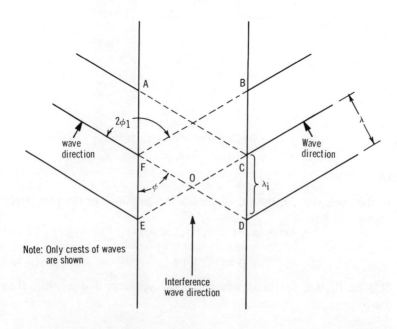

Note: Only crests of waves are shown

Interference wave direction

35. Parallel-plate propagation modes

The preceding discussions prepare us for considering propagation between parallel-conducting planes (a parallel-plate region). Two important types of propagation exist within this medium. Each depends upon the orientation of the E vector. If the E vector is perpendicular to the plates, the TEM mode exists—the same mode previously encountered in free space. However, we are primarily concerned in the next sections with the TE modes, in which the E vector is always transverse to the direction of propagation.

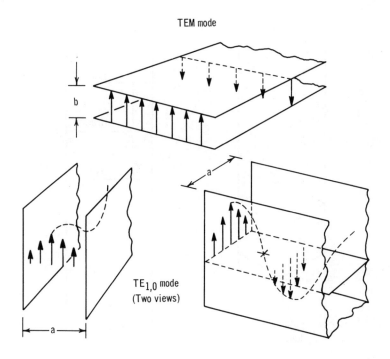

TEM mode

$TE_{1,0}$ mode
(Two views)

Before drawing the parallel between TE mode propagation and the preceding sections, we must recall the property of E fields in the presence of conductors. *No electric field can exist parallel to a perfectly conducting surface, at that surface.* Therefore, all TE mode fields must fall to zero at both side walls of the parallel-plate region. Across the plates, the amplitude distribution is sinusoidal. It is likewise sinusoidal along its length.

If one-half of a sine wave exists across the plates, the mode is $TE_{1,0}$; if N half waves exist, $TE_{N,0}$. The conditions for existence of these modes, we shall see later, depends upon the plate separation, a. On the other hand, it is always possible for the TEM mode to propagate between open-end parallel plates, regardless of the separation.

36. $TE_{1,0}$ representation as pairs of bouncing waves

One representation of the interior of a parallel-plate region propagating the $TE_{1,0}$ mode looks much like the interference region of our previous sketch of crossing waves. In that situation we had no boundary conditions to satisfy and arbitrarily drew the region such that the two waves were in phase at points C and D. In the present case, the two waves—successively reflected back and forth between the plates—are *constrained* to be 180° out of phase along the walls AFE and BCD. This constraint is necessary to satisfy the requirement of a zero E field parallel to the walls.

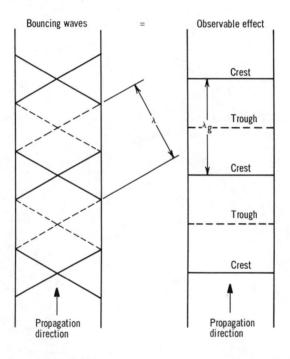

Calculations for guide wavelength, λ_g, and phase velocity, v_p, are exactly analogous to the calculations already made for water waves. As a consequence of zero E field at the constraining walls, however, a new feature appears—group velocity. This is the velocity of energy transport *in the direction of propagation* (parallel to the parallel plates).

The energy is carried in the zigzag path of bouncing waves, at the free-space velocity, c, and wavelength, λ. The group velocity, v_g, is a component of this velocity parallel to the plates. As we shall see, the phase velocity and group velocity are related by the equation

$$v_p v_g = c^2 \tag{2.35}$$

37. Satisfying the boundary conditions

It is instructive to follow in sequence the steps for representing, by bouncing waves, the $TE_{1,0}$ mode between parallel plates. Arbitrarily we select *a,* the plate separation, and ϕ, the angle of the reflected wave. Thus, we start by drawing AB, the crest of the first set of waves at the angle, ϕ. Next, since the *E* fields must fall to zero on both walls, troughs of the second set of waves must fall on both A and on B as shown. In order to achieve perfect cancellation everywhere along both walls, these two sets must have the identical wavelength as measured along the walls, and hence must be drawn at angle ϕ. At this juncture, *all* characteristics have been fixed. To make this clear, let us proceed a bit further. Draw CE, the next crest of the wave set AB, through C and parallel to AB. If we so desired, we could now fill in intermediate halfwaves and reproduce the figure of the preceding section. However, consider this uncluttered figure further. The free space wavelength, CF, is the perpendicular separation between successive wavefronts AB and CE; guide wavelength is the distance BC.

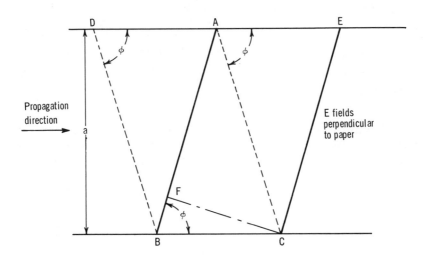

As ϕ approaches 90°, the angles ABD and BAC approach zero, like a carpenter's rule closing up. A little reflection will lead one to conclude that λ_g approaches λ, and that λ decreases (or, better, λ/a decreases).

As ϕ approaches zero, λ_g grows very large with respect to λ. At $\phi = 0$, λ_g is infinite, and the bouncing waves are parallel to the side walls, reflecting back on themselves. No energy is propagating down the guide. This condition is known as *cutoff* for the $TE_{1,0}$ mode. It is analogous to water waves impinging on a pier with $\phi = 0$, which we previously discussed.

38. Quantitative relationships for $TE_{1,0}$ mode

Trigonometry suffices to determine parameters of the $TE_{1,0}$ mode. We repeat a portion of the previous figure. From A, draw AD perpendicular to BC. The distance BD is $\lambda_g/2$. From D, draw DF perpendicular to AB. The distance DF is $\lambda/2$. The following relationships now pertain:

$$\text{From BDF: } \sin \phi = \lambda/\lambda_g \tag{2.36}$$

$$\text{From ADF: } \cos \phi = \lambda/2a \tag{2.37}$$

$$\text{From ABD: } \tan \phi = 2a/\lambda_g \tag{2.38}$$

In the time that wavefront AB proceeds to the right at velocity c so that point F on it moves to D, point B moves to D at the phase velocity, V_p. From Eq. 2.36, we get

$$v_p = c/\sin \phi \tag{2.39}$$

When F moves to D, the energy is carried in the direction of propagation to G, at group velocity. From triangle DFG,

$$v_g = c \sin \phi \tag{2.40}$$

Multiplying Eq. 2.39 by Eq. 2.40, we derive

$$v_p v_g = (c/\sin \phi)\,(c \sin \phi) = c^2 \tag{2.41}$$

Solving for $\sin \phi$ from the trigonometric identity, $\sin^2 \phi + \cos^2 \phi = 1$, and substituting in Eq. 2.36, we have $\lambda/\lambda_g = \sqrt{1 - \cos^2 \phi}$. Then, substituting in Eq. 2.37,

$$\lambda/\lambda_g = \sqrt{1 - (\lambda/2a)^2} \tag{2.42}$$

Note that as $\lambda/2a$ approaches zero, λ_g approaches λ, as we have previously seen. At cutoff for $TE_{1,0}$, as λ/λ_g approaches zero, it now appears that λ approaches $2a$. This value of λ is called λ_c, the cutoff wavelength.

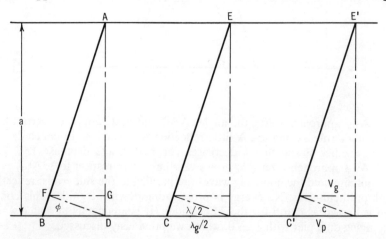

38. Quantitative relationships for TE$_{1,0}$ mode (Cont.)

RELATIONSHIP OF CUTOFF WAVELENGTH TO WAVEGUIDE LENGTH

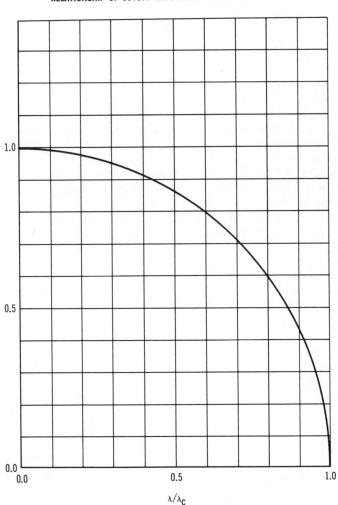

$\eta = \lambda/\lambda_g$

λ/λ_c

39. Index of refraction of parallel-plate region

From our definition of the index of refraction, n, and from Eq. 2.42 of the preceding section, we can write

$$n = \lambda/\lambda_g = \sqrt{1 - (\lambda/2a)^2} \qquad (2.43)$$

for the $\text{TE}_{1,0}$ mode of a parallel-plate region. Since λ_g always exceeds λ, v_p always exceeds c, and n lies between 0 and 1.0.

If a set of parallel plates is adjusted so that all plates are separated by the distance a, we have created an artificial dielectric medium. For the E vector of this medium parallel to the plates, the index of refraction is given by Eq. 2.43. For the E vector perpendicular to the plates, the TEM mode at velocity, c, obtains, and $n = 1.0$. If E impinges on this medium so that the wave front containing E is parallel to the plane of the interface but E itself makes an acute angle with the plates, E splits up into two components, perpendicular and parallel to the plates. These components travel at different phase velocities, and the artificial dielectric medium is therefore known as *birefringent*. If the acute angle happens to be $45°$ (so that the magnitudes of both TE and TEM mode waves are equal), the length, l, of the plates can be chosen so that the emerging phase of the $\text{TE}_{1,0}$ mode leads the TEM phase by $90°$. Upon leaving the plates, the components are therefore orthogonal in space and in time quadrature ($90°$ apart in phase). Therefore, after recombination, a circularly polarized wave emerges. Plates that accomplish this transformation are known as *quarter-wave plates*.

Similarly, plates of the proper length to permit the two modes to differ by $180°$ in phase are known as *half-wave plates*. The output vector, linearly polarized ,is rotated in space by $90°$ with respect to the incident.

QUARTER-WAVE PLATES

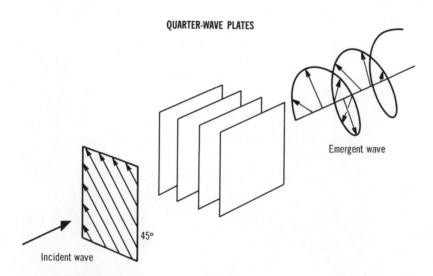

Emergent wave

45°

Incident wave

40. Rectangular waveguides

In considering propagation within parallel plates, we noted that $TE_{1,0}$ modes can exist if the separation, *a,* of the plates exceeds $\lambda/2$. Furthermore, since *E* lines can terminate on charges (which they induce when they fall normally on conductors), it is possible to insert conductive plates transverse to the parallel plates, without disturbing the *E* line configuration in the slightest. It is thus possible to isolate a region, ABCD, entirely enclosed by conductors. This region constitutes a rectangular waveguide.

The separation of the transverse plates, *b,* is usually chosen to be smaller than *a,* and most often, $b = a/2$. This dimensioning limits the number of higher order modes. In fact, if *a* lies between $\lambda/2$ and λ and *b* is less than $a/2$, only *one* mode, the $TE_{1,0}$, can exist. It is therefore called the *principal mode.* When thus limited to a single mode, energy within the waveguide may be guided around corners and bends at will. For this advantage, only a small price is paid in terms of energy losses in the waveguide walls.

Since the $TE_{1,0}$ configuration of *E* lines within waveguides is precisely the same as between parallel plates, all the quantitative relationships previously derived—for V_p, V_g, λ_g, *n,* and the like—apply as well to the waveguide case. We shall revert to a study of waveguides in greater detail in Chapter 4.

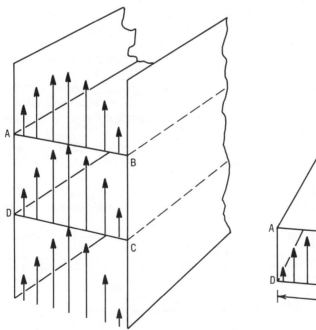

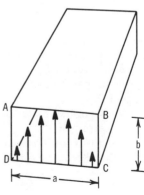

Summary of Chapter 2

Matter can be treated as if there were three "pure" states: perfect conductors, lossless dielectrics, and lossy material. At interfaces of matter, four boundary conditions determine field components: (1) tangential E are equal, (2) normal D are equal, (3) tangential H are equal, and (4) normal B are equal. In applying the above, account must be taken of charges or currents at the interface. Tubes of force terminate normally on charges and are repelled when they parallel currents on conductors.

The velocity of electromagnetic waves is slowed in dielectric media, and at interfaces, Snell's law establishes the direction of refraction. Fresnel's equations establish the magnitudes of reflected and transmitted waves. An important special case occurs at Brewster's angle, i, given by $\tan i = n$, when polarization is parallel to the plane of incidence.

A pair of bouncing waves satisfy boundary conditions between parallel conductive plates. From this concept, simple geometry serves to establish parameters for guided waves. VSWR, reflection and transmission coefficients—all useful tools in describing guided wave behavior—are defined in terms of sending and reflected waves.

Questions

1. How much energy is reflected from an open-end waveguide when the VSWR $= 1.6$? How much transmitted?

2. What is the dielectric constant of a lossless, nonferromagnetic medium if its propagation velocity is 6×10^7 m/sec.?

3. What is the angle of (a) reflection, and (b) refraction, for a plane wave incident upon a lossless dielectric at an angle of $20°$?

4. If E is perpendicular to the plane of incidence of a wave incident at $30°$ upon a lossless dielectric of $\epsilon_r = 4.0$, what fraction of incident voltage is (a) reflected? (b) transmitted?

5. What is Brewster's angle if ϵ_r at an air-medium interface is 3.24?

6. If an incident plane wave has an E vector polarization inclined $45°$ to the plane of incidence upon a perfect conductor and if $i = 30°$, what are the resultant ratios, E_R/E_I and E_T/E_I.

7. If a plane wave of intensity 1.0 volt/meter is incident normally upon a plane dielectric interface and $\rho = 0.02$ at a phase angle of $-170°$, what is the magnitude and phase angle of τ?

8. Calculate V_p, λ_g, n, and V_g for a $TE_{1,0}$ wave of frequency 5200 Mc/sec propagating in a rectangular waveguide whose inside dimensions are 2.0×1.0 in.

9. If parallel plates are 1.0 in. apart, and $\lambda = 1.5$ in., how long are quarter-wave plates?

10. For Case 1 (polarization perpendicular to the plane of incidence), derive the alternate expression,

$$\frac{E_r}{E_I} = \frac{\cos i - \sqrt{n^2 - \sin^2 i}}{\cos i + \sqrt{n^2 - \sin^2 i}}.$$

41. The rectangular horn

Suppose a source of electromagnetic energy is sending $TE_{1,0}$ mode energy to the right within a rectangular waveguide. Suppose further that the rectangular waveguide is abruptly terminated and that its open end is directed towards free space. The waveguide-free space interface constitutes a discontinuity in the transmission path of the energy. As the wave encounters this dielectric discontinuity, most of the energy will propagate into free space—be radiated, that is. However, an appreciable amount of energy will be reflected back toward the source, creating a standing wave in the waveguide, with a VSWR of perhaps 1.6 or so. If the object is to radiate as much of the energy as possible, this object can be furthered by flaring the waveguide in both dimensions—E and H planes—at its open end. Such a radiator is called a pyramidal horn, or simply, a horn.

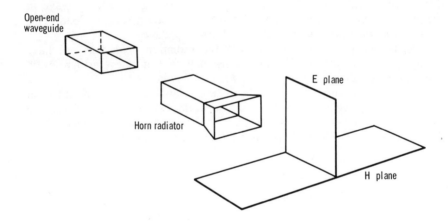

If the flare is sufficiently gradual and the face of the horn (its aperture) is sufficiently large, it is possible to effect a good (impedance) match at the interface so that reflections are minimized. VSWR's under a value of 1.1 can readily be achieved at any spot frequency.

Another object of flaring the horn is to narrow the radiated beam. When the flaring is made sufficiently gradual, phase aberrations across the aperture (departures from uniform phase) may be kept low—to values of $\lambda/4$ or less. With this restriction on phase aberration, the larger the aperture in terms of wavelengths, the narrower the radiated beam. Large phase aberrations across the aperture will spoil the beam.

The beam width in each principal plane of the horn may be controlled separately by flaring in that plane only. Horns flared in one plane only are known as E-plane sectoral or H-plane sectoral horns, depending, respectively, upon whether the E-plane or H-plane aperture is flared.

42. Radiation mechanism

The property of momentum of lines of force offers a physical picture of the mechanism of radiation. A wave traveling in a waveguide terminated by a horn propagates energy into space as shown.

Charges are carried along by the wave to the aperture of the horn. These moving charges constitute the propagation currents in the guide. At the aperture, the currents are abruptly terminated, and the momentum of the lines carries them a short distance out into space, still terminating on charges that have collected near the aperture. Then the wave arriving at the horn aperture alters its sense, and the charges terminating the preceding lines are neutralized, freeing their terminal points. These lines, instead of collapsing, join ends of opposite polarity, thus forming closed loops. As closed loops, they propagate to the right, pushed by the radiation pressure of the oncoming lines.

Not all incident energy is radiated. Some is reflected at the aperture discontinuity and returns toward the source, forming a standing wave in the guide. Some is stored near the aperture, creating a reactive load. This is the *induction field,* which influences horn impedance.

In the horn's immediate vicinity, the radiation field does not have exactly the same distribution and constancy that it does farther away. This region is called the *near field* or *Fresnel region.*

At large distances from the horn, the relative intensity of radiation *as a function of angle subtended by the horn,* does not change with distance from the horn. The horn electromagnetic "pattern" has already been established. This region is called the *far field,* or *Fraunhofer region.*

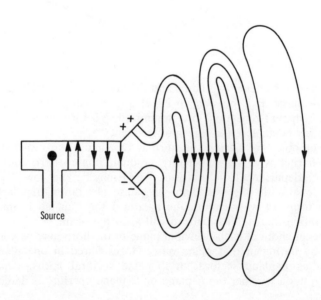

Source

43. Parallel-plate metal lens

With our accumulated knowledge, we are in a position, if we so desire, to design a practical lens antenna. We can design a horn to illuminate an array of parallel plates, stacked alongside one another and contoured to a lens shape. However, we wish merely to show how ray tracing can establish a lens contour to gain an insight into a lens antenna function.

Arbitrarily, we decide that (1) the illuminated face of the lens is to be contoured, (2) the exit face is to be planar, and (3) the index of refraction of the lens is to be less than unity. The last choice dictates that the lens should be thicker at the edges than at the center. This shape is just opposite to that of optical lenses, which are thicker at the center because n is greater than unity. Our objective is to contour the lens so that all rays emanating from an assumed point source will be in phase at the exit face of the lens. The rays are then said to be *collimated*.

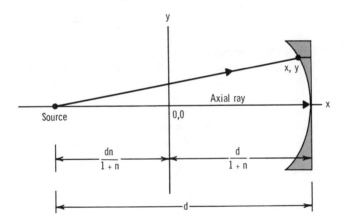

To accomplish collimation, we select an arbitrary off-axis ray and equate its electrical path length to that of the central on-axis ray, along the *x*-axis. Note that for this one ray the lens has zero thickness and the ray path is entirely in air dielectric, for which $n = 1.0$. We place the source at a distance, d, from the lens and select the origin of our coordinate system at a point midway between source and lens, as shown.

The incremental phase from source to lens planar surface is $2\pi d/\lambda$. The path for the ray at an arbitrary angle—which reaches the lens surface at an arbitrary x, y coordinate—is composed of an air path and a path through the lens of relative index n. The lens path is parallel to the axial ray. To the planar surface, the phase length is

$$\frac{2\pi}{\lambda}\left\{\sqrt{\left(x+\frac{dn}{1+n}\right)^2+y^2}+n\left(\frac{d}{1+n}-x\right)\right\} \qquad (3.1)$$

44. Elliptic metal-plate lens equation

Equating phase for the two rays to reach the flat surface of the lens,

$$\sqrt{\left(x + \frac{dn}{1+n}\right)^2 + y^2} + \frac{dn}{1+n} - nx = d \qquad (3.2)$$

Rearranging terms, and squaring both sides of Eq. 3.2, we get

$$x^2\,(1 - n^2) + y^2 = d^2\,(1 - n^2)/(1 + n)^2$$

With further juggling, this can be manipulated into the standard form for an ellipse, with major and minor axes falling on coordinate axes:

$$\frac{x^2}{\left(\dfrac{d}{1+n}\right)^2} + \frac{y^2}{\left(d\,\sqrt{\dfrac{1-n}{1+n}}\right)^2} = 1 \qquad (3.3)$$

The semi-major axis of the ellipse is $d/(1 + n)$; the semi-minor axis is $d\sqrt{(1 - n)/(1 + n)}$. The reason for our origin now appears: it was taken to coincide with the center of the major axis. The source, a distance $dn/(1 + n)$ from the center, coincides with one of the foci.

If one were now to build a lens following Eq. 3.3, it would get unreasonably thick at the edges if the aperture, *D,* were large (Fig. A).

To reduce size and conserve weight, one can "step" the lens, thus slipping the wave front by one full wavelength at the step (Fig. B). The new wavefront across *D* is indistinguishable from the unstepped phase front, but the behavior of the two lenses as a function of frequency differs.

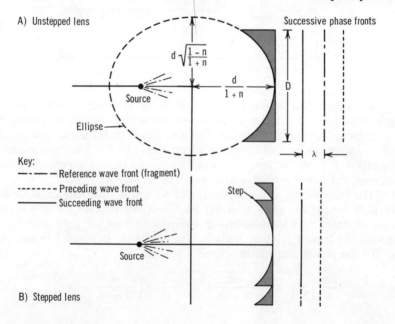

A) Unstepped lens

$d\sqrt{\dfrac{1-n}{1+n}}$

Source

$\dfrac{d}{1+n}$

D

Ellipse

Successive phase fronts

λ

Key:
— · — · — Reference wave front (fragment)
- - - - - - - Preceding wave front
——————— Succeeding wave front

Step

Source

B) Stepped lens

45. Stepped lens

The derivation of the equation for the stepped lens case follows closely that for the unstepped. In the present case, the phase of the two rays is permitted to differ by an integral number of wavelengths, $N\lambda$.

$$\sqrt{\left(x + \frac{dn}{1+n}\right)^2 + y^2} + \frac{nd}{1+n} - nx = d + N\lambda \qquad (3.4)$$

This, too, can be rearranged into the standard form

$$\frac{\left(x - \dfrac{n\,N\lambda}{1-n^2}\right)^2}{\left(\dfrac{d\,(1-n) + N\lambda}{1-n^2}\right)^2} + \frac{y^2}{\left(\dfrac{d\,(1-n) + N\lambda}{\sqrt{1-n^2}}\right)^2} = 1 \qquad (3.5)$$

This equation reduces to Eq. 3.3 when $N = 0$, as it should. As N takes on successive integral values, successive ellipses, each surrounding the one preceding, are formed. These are not concentric. Rather, the centers shift to maintain the source at a common focus for all.

Of practical interest is the thickness, t, in the x direction, of each step in the lens. From Eq. 3.5, the origin shifts to the right by $Nn\lambda/(1-n^2)$ whereas the semi-major axis increases by $N\lambda/(1 - n^2)$. The thickness of the Nth step is the sum of these distances.

$$\begin{aligned}
t_N &= \frac{N\lambda}{1-n^2} + \frac{Nn\lambda}{1-n^2} \\
&= \frac{N\lambda(1+n)}{1-n^2} = \frac{N\lambda}{1-n} \qquad (3.6)
\end{aligned}$$

Perhaps the significance of Eq. 3.6 will be best demonstrated by an enlarged view of the lens in the region of the step. A ray from the source falls on the lens at P and is refracted along the path, PQ. After refraction, the ray energy may split, one part traveling in the lens, the other parallel to it in air. These must differ in phase by λ. Therefore, $t - nt = \lambda$, from which $t = \lambda/(1 - n)$, which agrees with Eq. 3.6 for $N = 1$.

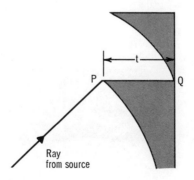

Ray from source

Antenna Theory

46. Limiting *f*-number of metal-plate lens

As in optics, the *f*-number of a microwave lens is defined as the ratio of focal length to aperture. For the elliptic metal-plate lens, the maximum aperture, D_m, is equal to its minor axis:

$$D_m = 2\left(\frac{d\,(1-n)+N\lambda}{\sqrt{1-n^2}}\right) \qquad (3.7)$$

The smallest *f*-number possible is d/D_m. Solving for d/D_m in Eq. 3.7, we get the limiting *f*-number for this type of metal plate lens.

$$f_{\lim} = 1/2\sqrt{(1+n)/(1-n)} - N\lambda/D_m\,(1-n) \qquad (3.8)$$

Even if Eq. 3.8 permits, *f*-numbers less than 1.0 should not, for practical purposes, be used. Several defects appear with small *f*-numbers, and these can be significant. Shadowing is one. The illuminated lens face is partly obscured by the step. This happens in both the *E* and *H* planes. In the *H* plane, continuous phase correction is impossible. The finite separation, *a,* of the parallel plates limits the correction to discrete values. If the theoretical correction required across the *a* dimension reaches or exceeds 90°, the efficiency of the lens-aperture extension is marginal. This imposes a limit on the half angle subtended by the aperture edges at the source, namely,

$$\theta \le \sin^{-1}(\lambda/4a) \qquad (3.9)$$

APERTURE PHASE LIMITATION

$$\frac{x}{a} = \sin\theta$$

$$\text{but } x \le \frac{\lambda}{4}$$

$$\sin\theta \le \frac{\lambda}{4a}$$

STEPPED METAL-PLATE LENS

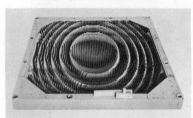

47. Paraboloid reflector antenna

Ray tracing techniques can also be used to determine the shape of a reflector antenna. Our object here, as with the lens, is to collimate all rays. For convenience, we choose the plane at which all rays are to have the same phase as that passing through the focus (the focal plane). The source is located at the focus, a distance F along the axis from the reflector.

The axial ray merely traverses the distance F twice to reach the reference surface. The arbitrary ray strikes the reflector at point x, y. On its return to the reference, we arbitrarily select the path parallel to the axial ray. Equating these paths, both assumed to be in the same medium, we get

$$\sqrt{(F - x)^2 + y^2} + (F - x) = 2F \qquad (3.10)$$

Upon squaring and rearranging, we derive the equation of the parabola:

$$y^2 = 4Fx \qquad (3.11)$$

As a figure of revolution, the parabola is known as the *paraboloid*. It is the form most often used for microwave antennas, despite the blockage that the source presents to reflected rays. Although the lens antenna does not suffer from this defect, it usually cannot compete with a paraboloid reflector in terms of weight, complexity, and cost.

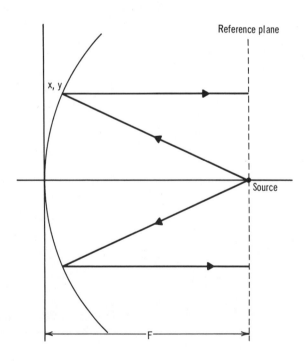

48. Far-field criterion

We have previously distinguished between three zones of an antenna: (1) the near field, or induction region; (2) the Fresnel zone, or transition region; and (3) the far field, or Fraunhofer region. We shall now pay particular attention to the last of these.

In the Fraunhofer region, the antenna pattern does not vary as a function of range. Therefore, the relative phases of the elemental Huygens sources on the aperture do not vary, as viewed from the observation point, as a function of range. In other words, the observation point is sufficiently distant from the antenna so that all rays to the point from the antenna can be considered to be parallel.

The condition to be fulfilled for the minimum range, R, that can be considered to fall within the far field range is known as the Rayleigh criterion. This criterion permits a maximum phase error of $\lambda/4$ across the antenna aperture. In the figure shown we impose the limitation,

$$\sqrt{R^2 + D^2} - R \leqq \lambda/4 \qquad (3.12)$$

Upon squaring, and neglecting $\lambda^2/16$, we derive the minimum far field range:

$$R \geqq 2D^2/\lambda \qquad (3.13)$$

The Fresnel zone extends out about as far as D^2/λ. At D^2/λ, the main beam characteristics are essentially formed. Only the subsidiary beams (side lobes) are appreciably different from those in the Fraunhofer region. The near zone extends only a few wavelengths from the aperture.

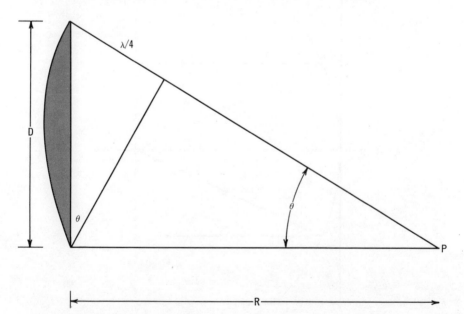

49. Beam width and shapes

A single Huygens' source has a hemispherical pattern, that is, energy flows out from this point source equally in all directions of a hemisphere. It is only when a *line* of Huygens' sources radiate all in phase that a narrow beam can be formed. The beam width is measured to half-power points (3 db) on either side of the peak. It varies inversely as the antenna diameter. An approximate formula for beam width, $\theta_{1/2}$, is

$$\theta_{1/2} \cong 65 \; \lambda/D \text{ deg} \tag{3.14}$$

The "constant," 65, depends somewhat upon the aperture illumination. For a uniform illumination across the aperture, a "constant" of 50.7 is appropriate; for an illumination heavily tapered (falling off rapidly from center to edge of aperture), a "constant" of 70 is better.

A *pencil beam,* such as that generated by a circular paraboloid, is narrow in both E and H planes. A *fan beam* is narrow in only one of the two. Beams of other configurations are known as *shaped beams*. One type of shaped beam frequently encountered is the *cosecant-squared beam*. It is a type of fan beam, narrow in one plane, whose orthogonal-plane power distribution follows the cosecant-squared function. In ground radar applications, the cosecant-squared pattern has the property of illuminating aircraft flying at a constant altitude with equal energy regardless of range.

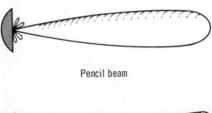

Pencil beam

Fan beam

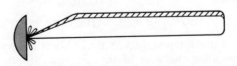

Cosecant squared beam

50. Antenna directivity gain

Useful as a standard reference radiator is the fictitious "point source," which radiates equal power in all directions (omnidirectionally). Our next objective is to compare the energy density radiated by a real antenna with that of the point source when both radiate equal total power, P_0 watts.

The angle subtended at the center of a circle of radius R by an arc length R is called 1 radian (57.3°). Similarly, the area or solid angle subtended at the center of a sphere of radius R by two orthogonal arcs each of length R is called 1 *steradian* (solid radian). Since the total area of a sphere is $4\pi R^2$, there are 4π steradians about any point.

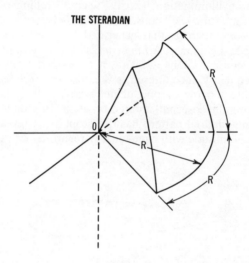

THE STERADIAN

If the point source is located at the center of the sphere, the energy density at the surface of the sphere is

$$P_0/4\pi R^2 \text{ watts/unit area} \qquad (3.15)$$

or,

$$P_0/4\pi \text{ watts/steradian} \qquad (3.16)$$

A real antenna's energy is concentrated within a directional beam. In the far field of the antenna, the energy density at the beam peak is greater than that for the point source by a factor G. Its density is

$$GP_0/4\pi \text{ watts/steradian} \qquad (3.17)$$

The factor G is the antenna directivity. In a less rigorous, but common usage, it is simply called the gain of the antenna. Strictly speaking, gain is differentiated from directivity in that gain takes into account any losses in the antenna. Large values of gain are usually expressed in decibels.

51. Gain of an aperture

Maximum antenna gain is achievable for any antenna when the illumination acoss its aperture is uniform in both planes. As we have seen, the beamwidth in one plane for uniform illumination is $\theta_{1/2} = 50.7\ \lambda/D$ deg $\cong \lambda/D$ radians. Therefore, for a square antenna aperture of area $A = D^2$, the steradian beamwidth is $(\lambda/D)^2$. If the antenna radiates P_0 watts, a good approximation to the energy density is

$$P_0/(\lambda/D)^2 = P_0 D^2/\lambda^2 = P_0 A/\lambda^2 \tag{3.18}$$

But, from Eq. 3.17, this density also equals $G\,P_0/4\pi$. Equating,

$$G\,P_0/4\pi = P_0 A/\lambda^2$$

or

$$G = 4\pi A/\lambda^2 \tag{3.19}$$

Equation 3.19 can be justified rigorously; it is an exact expression for gain. When the illumination is tapered, or when losses are encountered, a lesser gain is achieved. An efficiency factor, η, can be included to accommodate such effects.

$$G = \eta\ (4\pi A/\lambda^2) \tag{3.20}$$

Typical acceptable values of η range between 0.5 to 0.8, although much lesser values are sometimes tolerated.

If the aperture is rectangular and of dimensions D_1 and D_2, alternate expressions for gain in terms of E and H plane beamwidths can be obtained by substituting $A = D_1 \times D_2$ in Eq. 3.20:

$$G = \eta\ (4\pi/\theta_E\,\theta_H) \qquad (\theta \text{ in radians}) \tag{3.21}$$

$$G = \eta\ (41{,}254/\theta_E\,\theta_H) \qquad (\theta \text{ in degrees}) \tag{3.21A}$$

By defining gain as a ratio with reference to a point source (isotropic radiator), we have followed the practice of most authors. Occasionally an older work will refer gain to that of a half-wave dipole antenna. By our definition, the gain of the half-wave dipole is 1.6.

Another concept related to that of gain is that of the receiving or absorption cross section of an antenna, A, defined by

$$A = P_r/S \tag{3.22}$$

where P_r is the received power and S is the (uniform) power density in which the antenna is immersed. It is assumed by Eq. 3.22 that the antenna is matched to its load. Another equivalent expression for absorption cross section may be deduced by solving Eq. 3.19 for A, or $A = G\lambda^2/4\pi$. Copper losses, illumination losses, and mismatch losses are then lumped together to determine η, and in this case the losses are accounted for by recognizing a reduced aperture efficiency.

For large antennas the absorption cross section closely approximates the physical area of the antenna aperture. For small antennas, however, the absorption cross section may be quite a bit larger.

52. Antenna patterns

Let $F(\theta)$ be the variation of the field strength with the angle in an antenna's far field. The field pattern is taken at constant range, usually by rotating the antenna about its axis. In practice, the power pattern $P(\theta)$ —which is proportional to $F^2(\theta)$—is the measured quantity. Therefore, $P(\theta)$ is often referred to as the antenna pattern.

Across the aperture of a horn antenna, the E plane is uniformly illuminated, whereas H-plane illumination follows a cosine taper. For practical purposes, the two illuminations across a common aperture are assumed to be separable, that is, the pattern in each plane may be calculated independently.

The normalized E-plane field pattern of a horn, whose E-plane aperture is denoted by b, is

$$F_E(\theta) = sin\, u/u \tag{3.23}$$

where $u = \pi b\, sin\, \theta/\lambda$. "Normalized" simply means that the peak value is taken as unity. Similarly, the normalized H-plane pattern of a horn of H-plane aperture, a, is,

$$F_H(\theta) = (\pi/2)^2 \frac{cos\, u}{(\pi/2)^2 - u^2} \tag{3.24}$$

where $u = \pi a\, sin\, \theta/\lambda$.

The general characteristics of these functions are sketched below. Only half the pattern of the antenna (whose aperture is normal to $\theta = 0$) is shown, since the other half is symmetrical. The parameter u is taken as the abscissa rather than θ. On this scale it is seen that, for the same aperture size $(a = b)$, the beam width of a cosine illumination is nearly $3/2$ as broad as that for uniform illumination.

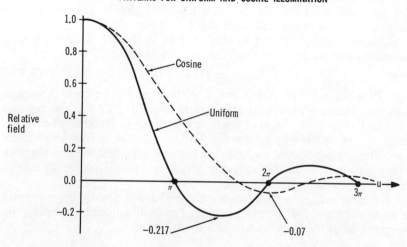

PATTERNS FOR UNIFORM AND COSINE ILLUMINATION

53. Side lobes

Not all energy delivered to the antenna terminals is radiated by the main beam. Side-lobe energy appears in accompanying beams of lesser magnitude. Generally it is desirable to suppress side-lobe energy to as low a value as possible. but this cannot be done without penalty. Although the uniformly illuminated aperture offers the highest gain, it is also affected by the highest side lobes. Tapering the aperture illumination reduces side lobes but also broadens the beam, dropping the gain.

For the uniformly illuminated aperture, the side lobes closest to the main beam (first side lobes) are 13 db down. Second and higher order lobes fall off in the ratio $1/u$. Patterns associated with a cosine illuminated aperture have their first side lobes 23 db down. Higher order side lobes fall off faster, or in the ratio $1/u^2$. In general, side lobes for a cos^n illumination fall off in the ratio $1/u^{(n+1)}$.

The table gives further pattern data on various types of aperture illuminations. The aperture limits lie between $x = \pm 1$.

PATTERNS ASSOCIATED WITH APERTURE ILLUMINATION

Illumination	Pattern	First side lobe level	
Uniform −1 0 +1	$\dfrac{\sin u}{u}$	13 db	
Cosine −1 0 +1	$(\pi/2)^2 \dfrac{\cos u}{(\pi/2)^2 - u^2}$	23 db	
Gabled −1 0 +1	$\left(\dfrac{\sin u}{u}\right)^2$	26 db	
Truncated sin x/x −1 0 +1 Edge taper	$\dfrac{*\text{Si}(u+a) - \text{Si}(u-a)}{2\,\text{Si}(a)}$	Edge taper	Side lobe levels
		0 db	13 db
		10 db	20.4 db
		20 db	25 db
		∞	26.4 db

*Si signifies sine-integral; a is a constant related to edge taper. An a of 3.32, 2.85 or π corresponds with 10, 20, and $-\infty$ db edge taper, respectively.

54. Phase errors across aperture

All previous patterns were assumed to result from aperture distributions having a constant phase. For beam-shaping purposes, phase across an aperture is sometimes made to vary in a controlled fashion. Either way, departures from intentional phasing are known as phase errors. Any phase error across an aperture along x may be expressed as

$$\Delta\phi = ax + bx^2 + cx^3 + dx^4 + \ldots \qquad (3.25)$$

where the constants $a, b,$ and the like, depend upon the magnitudes of the errors. The error involving the first power of x is called a linear error; the second power, quadratic error; and the third power, cubic error.

A linear phase error causes a beam tilt (see Fig. A). A quadratic phase error causes a broadening of the radiated beam and an increase in side lobe level (see Fig. B). A cubic phase error both tilts the main beam and distorts it (see Fig. C). Also the cubic error raises a high first lobe ("coma lobe") on the side of the beam nearer the normal to the aperture and reduces the other first lobe.

A linear phase error can be generated by rotating an antenna and its feed as a unit. A quadratic error results if the feed is moved along the focal axis toward the antenna. A cubic phase error occurs when the feed is moved transversely in the focal plane.

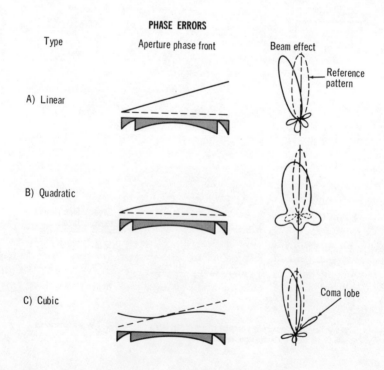

PHASE ERRORS

Type   Aperture phase front   Beam effect

A) Linear

B) Quadratic

C) Cubic

55. Relation of aperture distribution to antenna pattern

An attempt will now be made to provide an insight into how the antenna pattern is related to the aperture field. The antenna pattern is simply the vector sum of all the elemental Huygens' sources across the aperture, modified by the phase path from each source to the far-field point P. This modification neglects parallax, since all rays to a far-field point are assumed to be parallel. At the beam peak, $\theta = 0$, all of the source vectors seen at P not only are in phase, but sum to the largest possible magnitude. At a null in the pattern (see figure), the phases are distributed so that the vectors sum to zero.

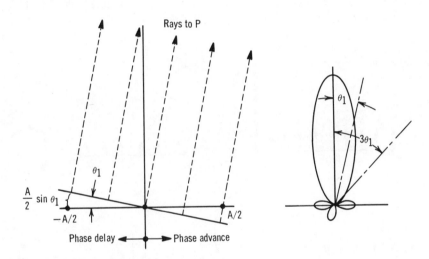

Let the antenna aperture lie between $\pm A/2$. At the center of the aperture we take the phase arbitrarily as zero ($\phi = 0$). For convenience we shall assume the aperture distribution to be uniform and in-phase. (If our antenna were less than perfect, or its beam shape a special one, the aperture distribution could very well have differed). We assume uniform phase to place emphasis on *relative* phases and how they must be modified to account for path length differences as a function of θ.

As viewed from P, when $\theta = 0$, all the ray paths from the sources are equal in length. However, when P is at angle θ_1, as in the figure, some rays travel a shorter path than the center ray, others longer. As viewed from P, relative phases over the left half of the aperture are progressively delayed (have a longer path to travel), whereas those over the right half are progressively advanced. The maximum phase delay at the aperture edge, $\Delta\phi$, is

$$\Delta\phi = \frac{2\pi}{\lambda}\left(\frac{A}{2}\sin\theta\right) = \frac{\pi A \sin\theta}{\lambda} \qquad (3.26)$$

56. Huygens' source vector addition at far field point

The magnitude and phase of the field at P is obtained for any θ by summing over all Huygens' sources. Each source we represent by the phasor, $e^{j\phi_n}$, where ϕ_n is the phase of the nth source relative to the center. All source field *vectors* are assumed to be parallel (linear polarization).

In Fig. A below, where $\theta = 0$ and $\phi_n = 0$ for all n, all phasors are cophasal. The resultant at P is the algebraic sum of all. In Fig. B, where $\theta = \theta_1$, the source phasors over the left half of the aperture are delayed by progressive counterclockwise rotations, and those over the right half are progressively advanced. Rotation of each is directly proportional to its distance from the aperture center. Figures C and D show relative phases at P for bearings of $2\theta_1$ and $3\theta_1$. The latter depicts a null.

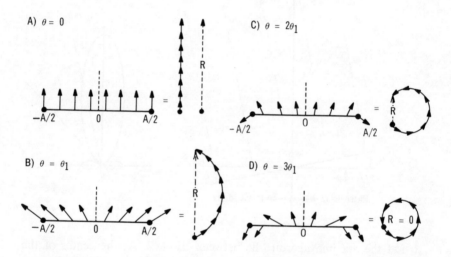

A number of important conclusions appear: (1) *The beam peak occurs at $\theta = 0$, when all phasors are cophasal.* (2) *The far-field phase of the entire main beam, peak to null, is constant*—This we deduce from symmetry when we sum all phasors by pairs that are equally distant from the aperture center. One phasor is rotated clockwise exactly as its pair is rotated counterclockwise. Therefore, left and right components of paired phasors cancel; only vertical components add. (3) *An abrupt 180° shift in phase occurs at the first side lobe and for higher order lobes*—This occurs when the sense of the parallel phasor components reverses, that is, whenever a null is traversed. (4) *A tapered aperture illumination has a broader beam than a uniform taper*—To prove this, reconsider Fig. D. Were the aperture edge phasors of smaller magnitude than the center, cancellation of vertical components would not be achieved; a greater θ would be needed to reach a null.

57. Horns used as feeds

We have seen that horns are used to illuminate larger lenses or re-flectors. In this usage the feed is called the primary radiator, and the larger antenna, the secondary radiator. The horn's popularity as a feed stems from the ease with which its E- and H-plane patterns may be inde-pendently controlled so as to illuminate the secondary aperture properly.

One principle of illumination that leads to reduced side lobes is to adjust the primary radiation pattern so that its equal intensity contours run parallel to the secondary aperture contour. For a square secondary aperture, this principle entails making the H-plane dimension of the horn $3/2$ larger than the E-plane dimension. (Recall that, for equal aperture dimensions, the H-plane pattern is $3/2$ as broad as the E-plane pattern).

To avoid pattern deterioration, the flare angle of the horn should be chosen so that the phase error across its aperture will be small. The phase error, $\Delta\phi$, across a horn with aperture, a, and axial length, l (measured to the intersection of the projected walls) is

$$\Delta\phi = (2\pi/\lambda)(\sqrt{(a/2)^2 + l^2} - l) \tag{3.27}$$

If $(2l/a)^2$ is large compared with 1.0, we can approximate $\Delta\phi$ by

$$\Delta\phi \cong \pi a^2/4\lambda l \tag{3.28}$$

Using Rayleigh's criterion, $\Delta\phi_{\max}$ should not exceed $\pi/2$. With these restrictions, the ratio of l/a should equal or exceed $a/2\lambda$. That is,

$$l/a \geqq a/2\lambda \tag{3.29}$$

Another restriction is that the secondary aperture should lie in the far field of the horn. If F is the focal distance, this requirement indicates that

$$2a^2/\lambda \leqq F \tag{3.30}$$

Since it is rare for all these criteria to be satisfied simultaneously, compromises are made.

PHASE ERROR ACROSS HORN

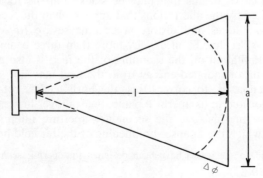

58. Multiple beams

Two or more beams may be generated in space by illuminating one common antenna aperture with several feeds mounted in the focal plane of the antenna. The horn dimensions are selected so that the main beams overlap. In order to accomplish this with the highest possible aperture efficiency, the horn are stacked contiguously, as shown in the figure.

Angular deviation of the secondary beam, θ, is nearly, but not quite, equal to the angle ϕ which the feed subtends from the center of the lens. The ratio of these two is known as the *beam deviation factor*. For large f-number antenna systems, the beam deviation factor approaches unity. The beam deviation factor diminishes from unity as the f-number gets smaller. For an f-number as small as 0.3, the beam deviation factor may decrease to 0.8.

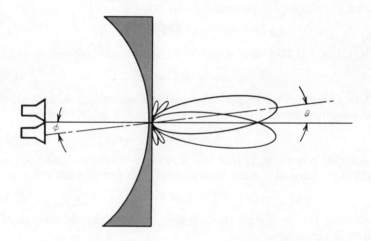

The number of beams that may be stacked in the focal plane of an antenna is limited by the aberrations that appear when the feed is moved off the focus. Coma lobes and distortion become severe for most antennas when the feed is "scanned" off axis by more than three beam widths.[1]

Another limitation on the scanning of the feed is also significant. An excessive amount of radiated energy from the feed may not even strike the secondary antenna. If, to correct this, the horn feed is rotated about an axis centrally located in its aperture plane, the spillover loss can be reduced. However, even for this case the secondary aperture illumination will be asymmetrical, which itself causes broadening of the far field beam.

[1] Special wide angle lenses have been designed that permit scanning more than twice as much.

59. Spillover power

Some feed energy spills past the antenna even for an on-focus feed. First, it is undesirable to illuminate the secondary aperture with side-lobe energy from the feed because first side-lobe energy is out of phase with that of the main beam. Second, it is not even desirable to locate the feed nulls at the periphery of the secondary aperture because this excessive taper results in a beam-broadening loss of efficiency in the use of the secondary aperture. These two effects—horn spillover power loss and efficiency of use of the secondary aperture—are opposite in their effect on gain. Therefore a compromise must be reached. Typical effects are shown in the figure.

The net effect on gain must take into account the product of these two effects. A broad optimum value of gain occurs when the edge taper is approximately -10 db in both the E and H planes. Recalling that the maximum gain of any aperture is $4\pi A/\lambda^2$, and that $10 \log 4\pi = 11.0$, we can express gain in decibels as follows:

$$G_{db} = 11.0 + 10 \log A/\lambda^2 \qquad (3.31)$$

For an aperture illuminated by a horn with equal edge tapers in both planes, we can write

$$G_{db} = G_{E,\ H} + 10 \log A/\lambda^2 \qquad (3.32)$$

This gain factor, $G_{E,\ H}$, is shown in the figure. Its maximum value is 9.7 db or 1.3 db below the theoretical maximum of an aperture not affected by spillover losses.

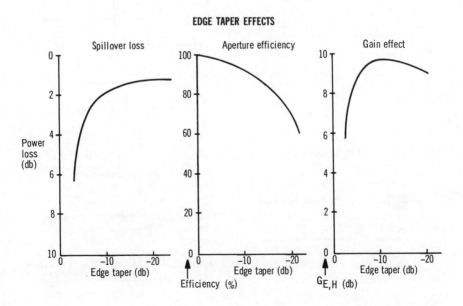

EDGE TAPER EFFECTS

60. Arrays

An antenna array consists of an ordered spatial arrangement of many like antenna elements connected together by a transmission line system. An array may afford cost or weight savings compared to one large antenna aperture, or it may have special (but costly) advantages, as when used for electronic beam steering. Frequently, although not always, the spacing between elements is constant. The elements may be distributed along a line (a line source) or along rows of lines in a planar array.

Basically, there are two ways of connecting elements of an array: (1) sequentially, from a single transmission line (Fig. A), and (2) in a parallel arrangement such as the corporate feed (Fig. B).

Our prime interest, as of the moment, is how to calculate the patterns of repetitive arrays. To this end, we shall first calculate the patterns of an array of equally spaced point sources. Utilizing this information and the convolution theorem, the patterns of an array of like antenna elements whose centers fall on the array of point sources can immediately be written down. Subsequently, we shall consider a limitation to the performance of arrays caused by a phenomenon known as *grating lobes*.

An example of an array of eight point sources—equally spaced and equally weighted—is shown in Fig. C, and the horn array derived from the convolution of the array with a single horn in Fig. D.

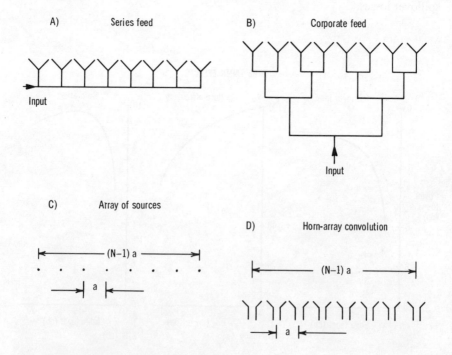

A)   Series feed

Input

B)   Corporate feed

Input

C)   Array of sources

(N–1) a

a

D)   Horn-array convolution

(N–1) a

a

61. Patterns of point sources — array factor

In calculating the far-field pattern of an aperture, we are interested in the *relative* phases across the aperture as viewed from a far-field point. The relative phase of a Huygens' source or a point source at a distance a from the center of the aperture is $\Delta\phi = 2\pi a_1 \sin\theta/\lambda = a_1 v$, where $v = 2\pi \sin\theta/\lambda$. Following previous notation, we represent this source by $e^{ja_1 v}$.

What is the field pattern of two point sources of equal magnitude (unity), in phase, and separated by equal distances, $\pm a$, from a common center? It is the sum of the two (see the figure), namely

$$e^{jav} + e^{-jav} = 2\cos av \qquad (3.33)$$

For the same two point sources, what is the field pattern if they radiate 180° out of phase (so that one is plus, the other minus)? It is their sum,

$$e^{jav} - e^{-jav} = 2j\sin av \qquad (3.34)$$

For an array of four in-phase, equal sources, separated by a distance of $2a$ and located at $-3a$, $-a$, $+a$, and $+3a$, we can now write the formula for the pattern by summing first the inner, then the outer pair of sources:

$$2\cos av + 2\cos 3av \qquad (3.35)$$

By use of trigonometric identities, it is possible to rewrite Eq. 3.35:

$$\sin 4av/\sin av \qquad (3.36)$$

Now we can state that the pattern of a line source array of N equally spaced, equal-strength point sources separated by the distance $2a$ is

$$\sin Nav/\sin av \qquad (3.37)$$

The patterns of arrays of point sources, as above, are known as array factors. The convolution theorem, which we shall next discuss, not only facilitates the calculation of real antenna arrays but provides a powerful tool for calculating factors themselves.

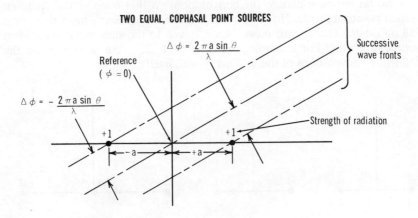

TWO EQUAL, COPHASAL POINT SOURCES

62. Convolutions

The pattern for an aperture source that is a convolution-derived array is the product of the individual patterns of the array and the element. Consider the pattern of the horn-array convolution in the last figure presented. The array is derived from the convolution of point sources with a single horn. If the horns were all oriented with their E vectors parallel to the line source, the pattern of the array would be

$$\left(\frac{\sin 8av/2}{\sin av/2} \right) \left(\frac{\sin u}{u} \right) \tag{3.38}$$

The above convolution, involving a single element, is the simplest kind. Next we shall consider a convolution of two elements with two. We shall rederive the pattern of four equal sources spaced apart by $2a$ (Eqs. 3.35 and 3.36). By the convolution process, *each* point of one of the arrays becomes the origin for the second array. The convoluted source is the sum of all second-array sources so spread out. This process is shown below (the asterisk connotes the convolution process).

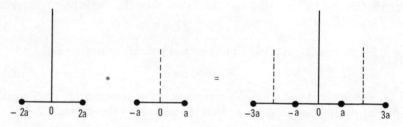

The patterns of the two-element arrays are $2 \cos 2av$ and $2 \cos av$. The pattern of the convolution (the four sources) is their product:

$$4 \cos 2av \cos av \tag{3.39}$$

Equation 3.39 is an identity equivalent to Eqs. 3.35 and 3.36.

So far we have chosen the convolutions so that none of the resultant source points coincide. However, it is possible to choose them so that some fall on others. Due regard must then be given to the sum of the coincident source strengths. For example, strengths of 1, 2, 1 are generated by the following convolutions of the 1, 1 array with itself:

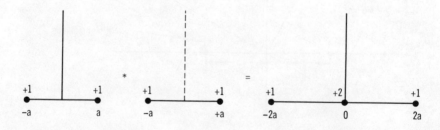

63. Grating lobes

The types of arrays considered thus far are called *broadside arrays* and contrast with *end-fire arrays,* which form beams along the axis of the array. All broadside arrays form only one major lobe if the element spacing is less than $\lambda/2$. If the element spacing greatly exceeds λ, many grating lobes are created. For a point-source array, those grating lobes equal the main lobe in magnitude. For a real antenna array, if the antenna element has sufficient directivity, grating lobes can be suppressed. In general, grating lobes are bothersome for real arrays whose spacings exceed λ.

When the element spacing of a point source array equals λ, three equal lobes exist—one main lobe and two grating lobes—which add in phase in the directions shown below.

GRATING LOBES

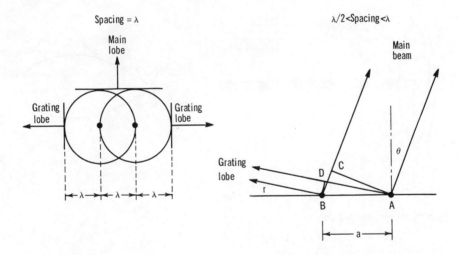

When the element spacing lies between $\lambda/2$ and λ, it may or may not be possible for a grating lobe to exist. Its existence depends upon the relative far-field phasing of the sources, that is, on how far off the array's normal the beam is scanned. When the grating lobe does exist, it appears on the side opposite the normal from which the beam is scanned, as shown in the figure. For the two sources to add in phase at both main-lobe and grating-lobe directions, we must have:

$$\overline{BC} + \overline{AD} = \lambda \qquad (3.40)$$

From Eq. 3.4, for spacing *a,* with the aid of trigonometry, we obtain

$$sin\ \theta = (\lambda/a) - cos\ r \qquad (3.41)$$

64. End-fire arrays

End-fire antennas can take a variety of forms. Polyrod, Yagi, and certain helical and traveling wave antennas fall into this category. To illustrate the principles involved, let us augment the three point sources, spaced λ apart and radiating in phase, by interspersing three cophasal point sources, equal in strength, but 180° out of phase with the first three. The broadside lobe disappears, for in the broadside direction complete cancellation takes place. The two grating lobes now become the main lobes. One of these can be eliminated by mounting a reflector a distance of λ/4 from one end of the line, thus forming an end-fire array element.

A) Configuration   B) Pattern

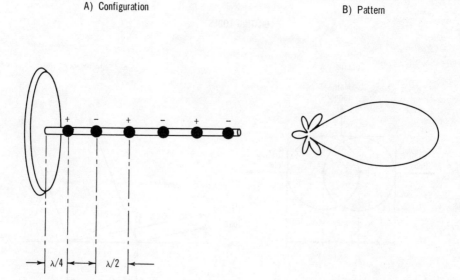

The width of the main lobe of the end-fire array is considerably reduced over that of a point source, but it is not as narrow as that of a broadside radiator of equal aperture. The end-fire beamwidth can be further reduced by increasing the length of the array. However, the benefits achieved may be marginal, for the gain increases only as the square root of the length of the array. A practical end-fire element, by itself, is unlikely to have a gain in excess of 15 or 20 db. To achieve greater gain, end-fire elements can be arrayed in a broadside fashion.

When arrayed in this fashion, end-fire elements are spaced apart so that their effective aperture areas, *A,* are contiguous. The effective aperture can be deduced from the formula for gain. Obviously, the effective areas of end-fire elements exceed their physical cross sections.

65. Hansen-Woodyard principle

When the element spacing is less than $\lambda/2$, it is possible to form one major end-fire lobe without the use of any reflector. One example is the end-fire radiator whose elements are spaced $\lambda/4$. For the phasing of successive elements that are end fed from a single transmission line and that are to be radiated cophasally with the radiation propagating outside the guide, the interelement phasing must equal $\pi/2$ radians. Along the axis of the array, the energy interferes constructively in the direction of propagation, and in the opposite direction, destructively. The pattern of two point sources, so spaced and phased, is therefore directional, as shown in the figure.

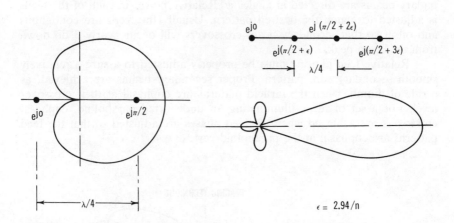

$\lambda/4$-SPACED END-FIRE ARRAYS

Doublet pattern   Hansen-Woodyard array

$\epsilon = 2.94/n$

If a number of $\lambda/4$-spaced doublets are stacked along a line and the successive inter-doublet spacing is $\lambda/2$ (a line of $\lambda/4$ elements), patterns of the doublets will be additive, and the resultant is a highly directional end-fire beam.

Despite the favorable gain achievable with the $\lambda/4$-spaced, $\pi/2$-phased end-fire array, this is surprisingly *not* the optimum condition. For a large number, N, of end-fire elements spaced $\lambda/4$ apart, Hansen and Woodyard have shown that, to achieve maximum gain, the inter-element phasing, $\Delta\phi$, should be

$$\Delta\phi = (\pi/2) + (2.94/N) \text{ radians} \qquad (3.42)$$

The pattern of the Hansen-Woodyard array has higher side-lobe energy and a narrower beam than the pattern of a $\lambda/4$ end-fire array of equivalent length and phased $\pi/2$ radians.

66. Shaped beams

Antenna beam patterns may be shaped by the following methods:
1. Interconnecting multiple feeds in the focal region of an antenna
2. Adjusting both the phase and the amplitude variations at the radiating aperture itself.

The design principles may be founded on either physical optics (diffraction theory) or geometrical optics (ray tracing). Our treatment will be restricted to geometrical optics.

Two conditions must be fulfilled whenever geometrical optics are employed:
1. The aperture must be large compared with λ.
2. Along each λ span of the aperture, the phase variation must be small compared with λ.

The imaging technique of geometrical optics is employed to locate multiple feeds in the focal region. The feeds are offset from the focal axis by angles θ (taking regard for the beam deviation factor) so that the secondary beams are directed at angles ψ. Relative power in each of the feeds is adjusted to match the desired pattern. Usually the feeds are contiguous and offset so that secondary beam crossovers will occur nearly 3 db down from the beam peaks.

Relative feed phasing must be properly adjusted to assure a relatively smooth secondary sum pattern. Proper secondary beams are achieved, as a rule of thumb, when the farfield patterns are cophasal at their crossover level. For a set of feeds illuminating an undistorted paraboloid, cophasal crossovers are achieved when the feed phases are adjusted so that the feed patterns are cophasal at the paraboloid vertex.

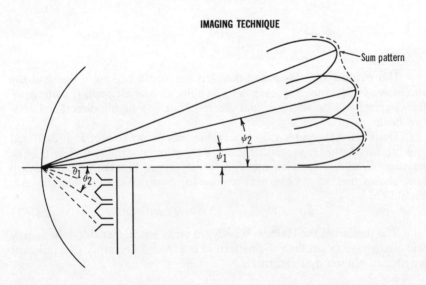

IMAGING TECHNIQUE

66. Shaped beams (Cont.)

Shaping a beam by deploying feeds in the focal region of a reflector is limited by aberrations to about plus or minus three beam widths. Wider-angle beam shaping is better achieved by contouring the reflector surface. A one-to-one relationship is established between ray directions, θ, of the feed and ray directions, ψ, of the secondary pattern. This is done by alloting x per cent of the feed power to synthesize the same x per cent of the secondary pattern power.

$$\frac{\text{Feed power between } (\theta_n \text{ and } \theta_{n+1})}{\text{Total feed power } (\theta_0 \text{ to } \theta_{\max})} = \frac{\text{Secondary power } (\psi_n \text{ to } \psi_{n+1})}{\text{Total secondary power } (\psi_0 \text{ to } \psi_{\max})}$$

The local reflector slope is then adjusted to direct the feed ray packet of energy to the proper secondary angle.

Both ground radar, whose purpose is to detect aircraft, and airborne radar, whose purpose is to paint a ground radar map, utilize cosecant-squared shaping of their antenna beams. Since the intensity of electromagnetic radiation, distant from its sources, diminishes as $1/R^2$ ($R = $ range), this beam shaping directs appreciable energy toward the horizon (or at the elevation angle of greatest range) and less energy at greater angles in order to compensate exactly for the drop off in intensity with range (neglecting earth curvature and atmosphere refraction).

Consider the radar detection of an aircraft. Let the aircraft fly at a constant altitude, h, and let ψ represent the elevation angle of the aircraft as viewed by the radar. Then, from simple geometry, $csc^2 \, \psi = R^2/h^2$. Assuming the antenna pattern is shaped to vary in intensity as $csc^2 \, \psi$, the product of the pattern variation by the range attenuation factor yields $1/R^2 \times R^2/h^2 = 1/h^2$, which is a constant, and independent of range. Hence the aircraft is illuminated with equal energy regardless of range.

SHAPED REFLECTOR TECHNIQUE

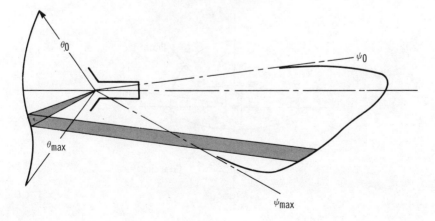

67. Reciprocity

The antenna transmit pattern—or directional variation in power across the antenna's far-field beam, $G(\theta)$—is measured by probing the field along the great circle of a sphere of constant radius. In practice, it is simpler, and completely equivalent, to determine the transmit pattern by rotating the transmitting antenna about its axis and measuring the variation in power at a fixed probe location in its far field.

The receive pattern of an antenna can be defined analogously to the transmit pattern, except that the probe is used as the radiator, and the antenna as the receiver. In practice, the receiving antenna is rotated about its axis, and the variation of received power, $P_r A(\theta)$, is recorded. $A(\theta)$ is known as the absorption cross section (that is, area) of the antenna. P_r is the received power per unit area.

The reciprocity theorem states that electromagnetic cause and effect can be interchanged in a linear passive network. Free space satisfies the properties of such a medium, and therefore one is led to the important conclusion: *Transmitting and receiving antenna patterns are identical in free space.* When scattering objects are located nearby—as they must be in any real situation—the theorem still applies, provided that antenna "aperture" is properly defined to include the significant scatterers. We may now generalize our previous expression for gain and state that the ratio $G(\theta)/A(\theta)$ is constant:

$$G(\theta)/A(\theta) = 4\pi/\lambda^2 \qquad (3.43)$$

The ionosphere—where free electrons exist in the presence of the earth's magnetic field—does not satisfy the conditions needed for reciprocity. Ferrite devices immersed in magnetic fields also constitute nonlinear media. Both ferrites and the ionosphere exhibit a nonreciprocal (one-way) property called Faraday rotation of the plane of polarization.

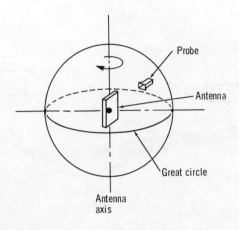

Probe

Antenna

Great circle

Antenna axis

Summary of Chapter 3

In the immediate vicinity (near field) of a radiating structure, the radiated beam suffers considerable distortion. This distortion persists but changes and diminishes with distance throughout the Fresnel zone out to a radius remote by D^2/λ from the source. At greater distances, in the far-field or Fraunhofer zone, relative intensity across the beam remains essentially unchanged. To ensure good fidelity of far-field beam characteristics even for low sidelobe levels, patterns are taken with a minimum separation between transmitter and test antenna of $2D^2/\lambda$. This ensures that the departure from the plane of the wavefront impinging on the test antenna is $\lambda/4$ or less (the Rayleigh criterion).

The paraboloid is a low-cost, effective secondary radiator. An electromagnetic horn is an effective primary radiator, since its E and H plane patterns may be separately controlled. Lenses have the advantage over reflectors of avoiding feed blockage. Compared to reflectors, however, they are difficult to fabricate and costly. Special beam shaping may be achieved —utilizing ray tracing—by special reflectors or lens designs.

The greatest gain of an antenna is achieved when its aperture distribution is uniform. A tapered aperture distribution will achieve lower side lobes at the expense of beam broadening. Phase aberrations may also result in beam broadening or steerage or both. Broadside and end-fire array antennas are useful. Their patterns may be calculated conveniently by means of the convolution theorem.

Questions

1. In the derivation of the lens equation, Eq. 3.1, the lens path of the arbitrary ray was taken parallel to the axial ray. Why?

2. Does the addition of a constant thickness to the planar side of an elliptic metal plate lens affect its focusing properties?

3. Show that the stepping thickness of a lens equals $\lambda/(\cos \theta - n)$ if, instead of emerging perpendicular to the planar face, the rays emerge at angle θ.

4. Verify that the angle of incidence equals the angle of reflection for an arbitrary ray of a paraboloid antenna.

5. What is the minimum axial length (to satisfy Rayleigh's criterion on phase) of a pyramidial horn whose E-plane aperture equals 10λ? Estimate how far down its third side lobes are, in decibels.

6. How much linear phase error is required across an aperture to steer its beam by half the antenna beamwidth?

7. Estimate the gain of a 50λ by 60λ lens fed by a horn if the edge taper in both planes is (a) 5 db, (b) 10 db, (c) 20 db.

8. Prove that grating lobes first become possible if $\theta \leq \sin^{-1}(\lambda/a - 1)$.

9. Calculate the pattern of three in-phase point sources of separation $2a$ and strengths 1, 2, 1. Prove that for equal separations, $2a$, and source strengths, $(1 + 1)^n$, the pattern is $cos^n\ (av)$.

68. The paraboloid

We have already mentioned that the paraboloid reflector antenna enjoys greater usage than any other type, and for good reason. To mention but a few of its advantages: it is much lighter than a lens; it is not subject to grating lobes as is an array; and, by virtue of its rotational symmetry, it is economical to manufacture and its contour accuracy is easily checked. One shortcoming of the paraboloid, however, is that the feed and the feed transmission line constitute an obstacle in the path of the radiated energy. The chief effect of this obstacle is to raise the side lobe levels of the antenna. To minimize this effect, it is desirable that the obstacle area constitute less than one per cent of the aperture area, although percentages as high as 10 or even 15 per cent are sometimes tolerated.

One technique for minimizing the blockage is to run the transmission line to the feed from the center (vertex) of the paraboloid. A "splash plate" feed is then mounted off the end of the transmission line to redirect the primary energy back toward the reflector. Another technique is to illuminate an asymmetrically cut paraboloid. For example, the reflector may constitute only the upper half of a paraboloid. The "offset" feed is actually located at the focus, but it is tilted upward so as to illuminate the reflector properly. By this means, the radiated energy bypasses the feed.

The disadvantage of the center feed technique is that its power-handling capacity is reduced below that of the waveguide, and of the offset feed technique, that its patterns are not as good as the symmetrically cut paraboloid.

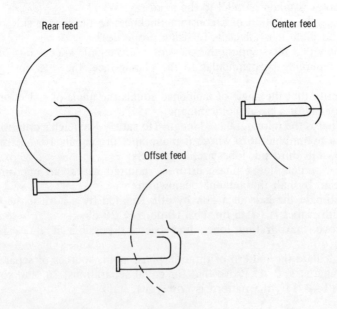

Rear feed

Center feed

Offset feed

69. Aperture blockage

The principle of *superposition* permits one to estimate the effects of aperture blockage upon side-lobe levels. Blockage effects can be determined by postulating an imaginary source, occupying the blocked space, that has an aperture field exactly equal but *opposite in phase* to the incident field. Destructive interference or shadowing occurs over the hypothetical aperture. The effects in space may be determined by calculating the far field of the postulated source and superposing it vectorially on the unperturbed far field.

If blockage area is small, reduction in main lobe power by the postulated radiator (which is out of phase with it over the main beam) may be neglected for a first-order approximation. Again, if blockage aperture is small, its pattern is broad compared with the main beams. The blockage pattern thus encompasses the first-side lobes of the main beam. Since these are 180° out of phase with the main beam, they are in phase with the blockage radiation beam. Hence, first-side lobe levels are raised.

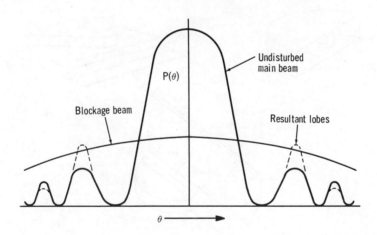

The principle of superposition permits the two patterns to be calculated separately and then added to determine the net effect. Suppose, for example, that we are dealing with a cosine-illuminated aperture whose first lobes are −23 db. Furthermore, assume that the feed blockage physically is 1 per cent, but that the average blockage power intercepted is twice the average illumination of the secondary aperture. In view of the relative illumination, and since gain is proportional to area, the effect of the blockage radiator is weighted at 2 per cent of the gain of the main antenna. Converting power to field strength and adding, we get the resultant side lobe level:

$$\text{Resultant} = 0.0447 + 0.050 = 0.0947 \text{ volts/unit length}$$
$$= -20.5 \text{ db}$$

70. Parabolic line sources

A number of variations of the parabola have found frequent application as line-source antennas; a few of the more common will be described. A parallel-plate transmission medium terminated at one end by a parabolic reflector constitutes one such. If the plate separation, b, is less than $\lambda/2$, so that only the TEM mode can propagate, the line source is known as a *pill box*. In order to reduce the E-plane beamwidth of such an antenna, a horn flare may be added to the aperture. If the plate separation is made greater than $\lambda/2$, it can accommodate either TEM or TE modes. In this event, the plate separation is usually chosen to equal several λ, and the antenna is known as a *cheese*. (These odd names were contributed by the British during World War II).

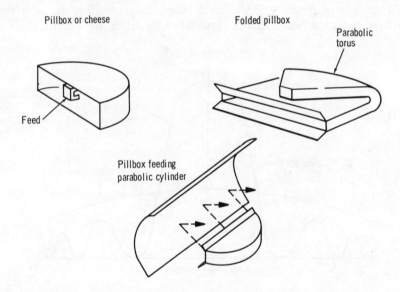

Both the pill box and cheese antennas suffer from feed blockage. The folded pill box, however, is a variation that avoids feed blockage altogether. The folded pill box has two adjacent layers of parallel-plate region, one atop the other, connected by a toroidal bend. A toroidal bend is a U-shaped bend of the parallel plates so devised that the normal separation of the plates remains constant. The toroidal bend is made along a parabolic arc. Feed energy from, say, the upper half spreads out and is reflected from the parabolic torus to form a collimated line source on the lower half.

Any one of the above line sources may then be employed to feed a large parabolic cylinder antenna—itself another variation of the parabola generated by moving a fixed parabola parallel to itself along a straight-line generatrix.

71. Cassegrain optics

Another important variation of the paraboloid for avoiding aperture blockage is based upon the use of Cassegrain optics. The Cassegrain antenna is the direct microwave counterpart of the Cassegrain telescope. Its construction is indicated in the figure. The feed, mounted near the vertex of the paraboloid, illuminates a hyperboloid reflector located on the focal axis at a distance from it somewhat shorter than the focal distance. The hyperboloid reflector is so placed that the feed rays which reach the paraboloid appear to come from the focus.

It would appear from the figure that the aperture blockage has been increased rather than decreased. And, indeed, this is the case for a conventional Cassegrain antenna, because the hyperboloid reflector is larger than the feed horn. The conventional Cassegrain antenna is used when transmission lines to feed horns must be kept electrically short.

The hyperboloid blockage of a Cassegrain antenna can be avoided. Recall that when the E vector is perpendicular to a stack of parallel plates it will propagate right through them in the TEM mode regardless of plate separation. On the other hand, when the E vector is parallel to the plates and their separation is less than $\lambda/2$, reflection must occur because propagation in the principal mode is cut off. Such plates can easily be shaped to a hyperboloidal contour. If the plane of polarization of the E vector could somehow be rotated at the paraboloid after reflection from the hyperboloid, the problem could be solved. And it can be.

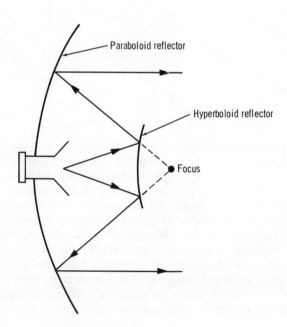

72. Grating reflectors

A set of parallel plates, with spacings adjusted below cutoff, is but one example of a class of media that are both transmissive and reflective, depending upon polarization. Sets of parallel elliptical slats, round rods, or even flat ribbons all comprise reflecting gratings and also fall into this class. To achieve the same degree of reflectivity, the flatter members usually must be set closer together than those possessing depth. Antenna surfaces frequently are constructed of reflective gratings to lessen weight and reduce wind loading. Such surfaces are restricted to a single illumination polarization. Another technique for reducing reflector weight is to drill or punch perforations into the solid reflector surface. Perforations serve as reflectors for any polarization, provided that the hole perimeter is less than $\lambda/2$.

Parallel plates   Round rods   Ribbons

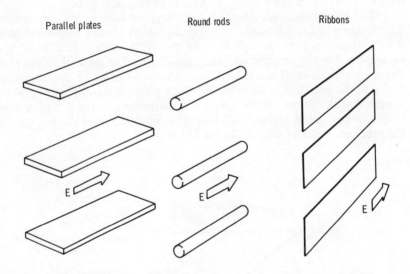

A grating of ribbons—offset by a distance of $\lambda/4$ in front of a paraboloid reflector in such a way that the line of ribbons is everywhere oriented at 45° to the incident E vector—constitutes a device to rotate the E vector by 90°. Assume the feed horn energy of a Cassegrain antenna to be vertically polarized. A hyperboloid sub-reflector may be constructed of a vertical ribbon grating supported on an electrically transparent plastic. Feed energy is redirected by the sub-reflector toward the main dish. At the 45° grating, only the component transverse to the grating propagates through it, the parallel component being reflected with an attendant 180° phase change upon reflection. One-half wavelength later, both components rejoin to form a resultant E vector rotated by 90°. The sub-reflector is then transmissive to the rotated E field, and sub-reflector blockage is avoided.

73. Dual lens and dual reflector

Many unusual devices worthy of mention have been based upon the versatility of gratings. It will be possible to present only a few suggestive applications beyond those already considered.

As one example, suppose that a secondary antenna aperture is comprised of two lens antennas occupying a common volume. The two antennas are isolated from interference with one another by the use of orthogonal polarizations. For one polarization, the lens focuses a point source, and for its orthogonal polarization, a line source. (Such a dual lens antenna is shown on the next page.) Assume, furthermore, that the two beams emanating from the common aperture are required to point in the same direction. A seeming design obstacle arises, for both antenna feeds should occupy a common focus. Although this does not pose an impossible problem, it proves troublesome, and the alternative solution of using a polarization selective grating is more elegant and satisfactory. The grating permits a *virtual image* of the line source to appear at the focus, whereas the real source does not.

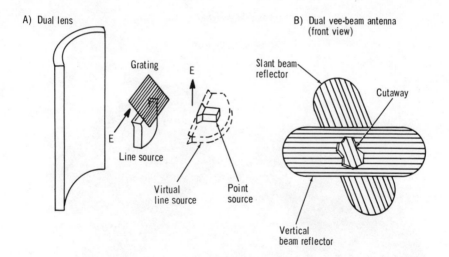

A) Dual lens

Grating

E

Line source

E

Virtual line source

Point source

B) Dual vee-beam antenna (front view)

Slant beam reflector

Cutaway

Vertical beam reflector

Still another example of the use of gratings is exemplified by the dual reflector antenna. Again, the two antennas occupy a common volume in space and are segregated by polarization. The reflectors consist of overlapping horizontal and vertical gratings, respectively. The surface of each is shaped to form a cosecant-squared beam. One reflector is rotated about its focal axis, however, so that the two fan beams form a vee in space. This type of antenna is used with a height-finding radar. The proper feed illumination of its inclined reflector constitutes an interesting feed problem, to which we shall refer later.

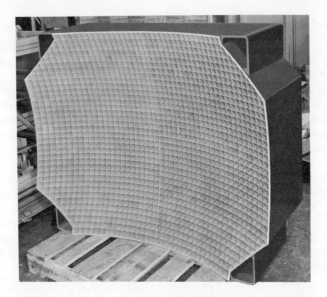

DUAL LENS ANTENNA

A Pillbox Source   B Foster Scanner   C Line Source Radiator

FOSTER SCANNER FEED

74. The Foster scanner

The function of the Foster scanner (bottom photo, left-hand page) is to scan a line source input, that is, to cause the line source beam to oscillate back and forth in space. The Foster scanner energy traverses a parallel-plate region formed by the space between two concentrically mounted cones, one inside the other, the second being slightly larger. Scanning is accomplished by a constant-speed rotation of the inner cone within the outer. Energy is directed to follow a path through the inner cone, which is split along a diameter to form a parallel-plate region and is supported only at both ends. Constraint of the energy so that it will follow the proper paths through the scanner is accomplished by means of gratings separately attached to the rotor and to the stator. The rotor and stator gratings (or "teeth") are interleaved so that they may pass one another without mechanical obstruction. During the passage time, the scanner is not electrically usable; this is called the *scanner dead time*. The figure below shows the scanner assembly, a cross section for two different instants of time (positions of the rotor), and a longitudinal section.

Assuming counterclockwise rotation, the first cross-section shows the minimum pathlength from input to output, immediately after dead time. In the second, the rotor has advanced one-half turn further, and the path lengths have increased for all rays. However, the path lengths at different positions along the cone have increased by different amounts, proportional to the local cone diameter. Thus, a linear phase error has been introduced, and the line-source beam has been caused to scan.

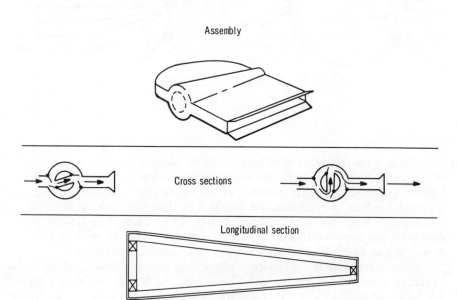

Assembly

Cross sections

Longitudinal section

75. Luneberg lenses

Another large class of antennas is based upon focusing properties first expounded by the mathematician, R. K. Luneberg. Luneberg's derivation applies to a spherical dielectric antenna that collimates a beam when a feed is placed at any position on the surface of the sphere. The dielectric constant of the sphere varies only as a function of its radius. Luneberg has shown this to be

$$\epsilon_r = 2 - (r/R_o)^2 \qquad (4.1)$$

where r is any radius and R_o is the maximum radius.

The central ray traverses the densest path and is slowed the most; peripheral rays cover the least dense path and are the least slowed. The optics is perfect in the sense that, theoretically, no aberrations exist for any position of the feed. In practice, however, certain difficulties arise that bring about less than perfect optics. It is difficult to achieve the dielectric constant variation.

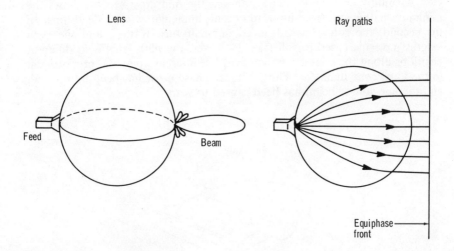

Good approximations have been made by building the lens as a series of concentric, spherical shells of fixed dielectric constant. Each shell may consist of a foam dielectric material of the appropriate density. Another approach has been to synthesize the variation by the embedment of metallic obstacles, such as spheres, in a foam matrix. In all cases it is difficult to synthesize the conditions, $\epsilon_r \cong 1.0$. Frequently a very thin shell of high dielectric—an outer skin—is used for reasons of mechanical support.

Notwithstanding the difficulties, many very practical and serviceable Luneberg antennas have been built. Their major defect is relatively high side lobes, which are caused by peripheral ray bunching.

76. Luneberg variations

Variants of the basic Luneberg antenna are too numerous to cover completely or to ignore. Perhaps the simplest is the modification which converts it into a wide-angle, high-gain, retrodirective reflector. This feat is accomplished by substituting for the feed a metallic, reflective "patch" that is affixed directly to a large portion (up to a hemisphere) of its surface. Beams that fall upon this Luneberg are focused upon the metallic patch and are reflected back toward the source at high gain, with the reflected beamwidth commensurate with the Luneberg diameter.

Two-dimensional versions of the Luneberg find practical uses. A direct analog consists of the parallel plate-region between two circular metallic disks, where the dielectric constant follows the Luneberg functional relationship. Still another type is the Rinehart version. The Rinehart-Luneberg simulates the index of refraction required by enforcing geodesic ray paths of proper length between parallel plates. The plates are deformed, retaining constant separation, into a helmet shape. The central ray takes the straight route over the top; divergent rays take less steep paths. However, all paths to a reference plane are precisely equal. Rays take curved paths, called geodesics, which, for each angle from the feed, result in minimum propagation time (Fermat's principle).

The small-circle Luneberg is a variant derived by Eaton. It describes the dielectric constants as functions of the radius r for each of two contiguous and concentric sphere—an inner of radius r_o and an outer of radius R_o. For the inner sphere the equation is

$$\epsilon_{r_i} = \frac{2 - r/R_o}{r/R_o} \qquad (4.2)$$

and for the outer,

$$\epsilon_{r_o} = \frac{2 - r^2/r_o R_o}{r_o/R_o} \qquad (4.3)$$

Rinehart-Luneberg   Section through Rinehart-Luneberg

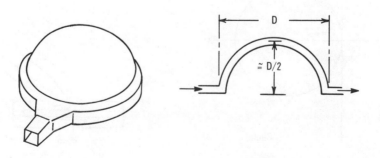

77. Geodesic antennas

Geodesic antennas were conceived prior to Luneberg antennas in an attempt to provide wide-angle scanning of an antenna beam by movement of the feed alone. One of the earliest geodesics was the R-2R, a circular parallel-plate region joined to another of double radius. Later designs attempted to utilize symmetry properties for wide-angle scanning. Such geodesics, however, must forego aberration-free optics. Thus, circularly symmetric geodesics have lower aperture efficiency and, to a large degree, have been supplanted by the Luneberg antenna. However, special feeds have been developed to compensate for the quadratric phase errors of the secondary circular or spherical apertures.

Consider the two-dimensional geodesic flushmounted on the surface of an aircraft when it is required to scan a fan beam over 360° in azimuth. Focusing properties of this antenna rely upon matching a parabola to a portion of a circle. The focal length of the parabola, which closely approximates the circular arc, equals half the circle radius.

The equation of the parabola with $F = R/2$ is

$$y^2 = 4Rx/2 = 2Rx \qquad (4.4)$$

When the circle in Fig. A is displaced a distance R to the right of the origin, its equation is $(x - R)^2 + y^2 = R^2$. This reduces to

$$y^2 = 2Rx - x^2 \qquad (4.5)$$

which approximates Eq. 4.4 when $x < R$. A practical version of the scanner is shown in Fig. B, where the toroidal bend eliminates feed blockage and reverses the beam direction.

CIRCULAR APPROXIMATION OF PARABOLA

A) Common-focus conics

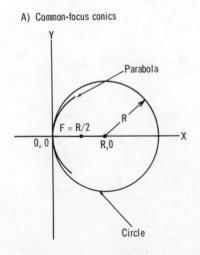

B) Geodesic scanner

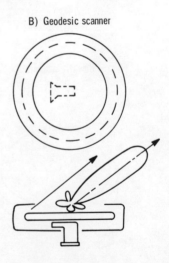

78. Helical antennas

A single conductor, wound in the form of a helix and fed from one end, constitutes a useful antenna for radiating a circularly polarized field. The screw sense of the radiation follows that of the winding. In satisfying antenna boundary conditions, the *E* vector must terminate normally upon the charges carried by the winding. Consequently, it rotates as the wave progresses, its end point tracing out the physical helix of the antenna and continuing at the same rate in space.

Two different modes of operation characterize the helical antenna: (1) the *normal* mode exists when the dimensions of the antenna are small compared with the wavelength, and (2) the *axial* mode exists when the perimeter of a single turn is comparable to one wavelength.

1. *Normal mode*—For this mode, the beam shape is omniazimuth (a beacon pattern of equal intensity in a horizontal plane covering 360° in azimuth) with very little energy appearing along the axis. As viewed along the antenna axis, the *E* vector rotates many turns per linear wavelength along that axis. Destructive interference therefore ensues. As viewed radially, in a plane perpendicular to the antenna axis, all the *E* vector components along the axis are nearly in phase at one instant of time (because the antenna, short compared with the wavelength, has many turns per wavelength). At another instant of time, 90° in phase later, all *E* vectors are still cophasal, but their *spatial* orientation has altered by 90°. Thus, the conditions for circular polarization are satisfied.

2. *Axial mode*—A pencil beam directed along the antenna axis is generated by this mode, with little energy directed radially. An instantaneous snapshot of the radiation along the antenna axis, viewed radially, sees all possible vector orientations, with consequent destructive interference. Axially, the vector rotates once per cycle, that is, it is circularly polarized. All circularly polarized antennas are blind to that radiation which is of opposite screw sense.

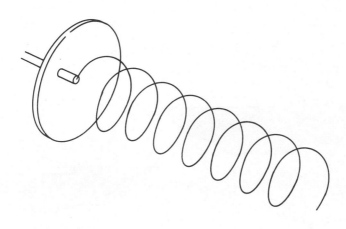

79. Surface waves

In a plane orthogonal to the narrow beam of the circular geodesic antenna previously described, a degree of end-fire beam shaping occurs. This end-fire effect may further be enhanced by the emplacement of a flat sheet of dielectric material over the antenna surface to form a slow-wave radiator. Energy is guided by the dielectric-conductor pair along its surface in a mode of propagation known as a *surface wave*. The velocity of propagation is slower than in free space.

The lowest order surface-wave mode is a hybrid (neither TE nor TM) that resembles a distorted TEM mode (see Fig. A). The distortion, typical of all surface-wave modes, is such that a component of the Poynting vector ($E \times H$) is directed into the dielectric rather than pointed entirely in the direction of propagation. The surface wave is thus bound to the dielectric interface. The surface wave can be restricted to the lowest order hybrid mode by limiting the slab thickness, t_0, to

$$t_0 \leq \lambda/4\sqrt{\epsilon_r - 1} \tag{4.6}$$

When the surface loading is heavy, most of the energy is captured by and passes through the dielectric rather than through the air. Very little, if any, radiation occurs except at the terminal edges of the slab. When the loading is varied, for example, by tapering the slab thickness, energy may be radiated along the slab's entire surface.

A practical embodiment of the surface-wave antenna is shown for a beacon antenna in Fig. B. Beam shaping, however, does occur in elevation by virtue of an end-fire effect. If the beacon antenna shown is mounted on a large ground plane, an uptilt away from the ground plane occurs for the entire omniazimuth lobe.

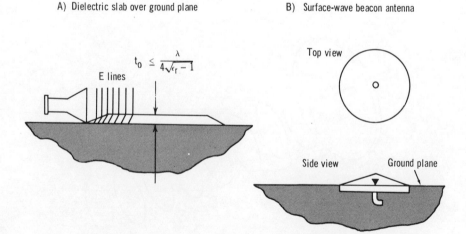

A) Dielectric slab over ground plane

B) Surface-wave beacon antenna

80. Channel guide radiator

One convenient method of loading a waveguide is to fill it, partially or completely, with a dielectric. The *b* dimension of a rectangular waveguide, so filled, must be reduced, if the propagation of higher order TE modes is to be avoided. The dielectric-filled waveguide may be converted to a channel-guide radiator by stripping away one broad face of the guide and introducing a linear taper of diminishing *b* dimension where the plastic is exposed. To effect a better impedance match, the plastic may also be tapered where it enters the enclosed waveguide.

A typical pattern of such a radiator is shown in the figure where the energy at the ground plane is some 6 db below the peak, which occurs about 20° above the ground plane. Scalloping of the pattern is caused by the interference of two line sources generated at the waveguide discontinuity and the terminal discontinuity.

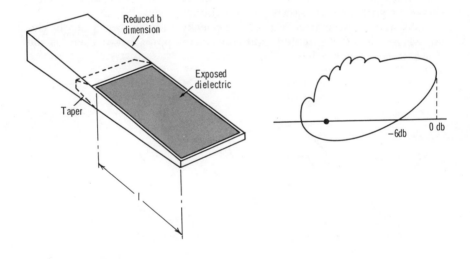

The length, *l*, of the taper is not critical, and the pattern varies only slowly around its optimum length. An optimum length occurs when the surface-wave energy and the free-space energy propagating over it differ in phase by 180°. When the free-space and surface-wave lines of force differ in phase by 180°, the free-space lines break away and radiate. Guiding is therefore no longer effective. If $\lambda_{\bar{g}}$ is the average wavelength of the surface wave over length *l*, and $\bar{\beta} = 2\pi/\lambda_{\bar{g}}$, the optimum length is

$$l = \pi/(\bar{\beta} - k) \qquad (4.7)$$

81. Leaky waveguide radiators

The channel-guide radiator is one example of a class of slow-wave, leaky end-fire radiators. The traveling wave propagating along its aperture continuously loses energy to radiation along its length. This behavior contrasts with that of end-fire radiators, in which discrete elements are excited in proper phase to radiate in a specified direction. However, not all leaky waveguide radiators are slow-wave structures. Indeed, a most elementary type of fast-wave, leaky waveguide radiator is achieved by cutting a shallow vee opening in the broad face of a waveguide.

As noted, the phase velocity inside the rectangular waveguide is $V_p/c = \sqrt{1 - (\lambda/2a)^2}$. The beam peaks at the angle ψ_p, for which the free space and guided energy add in phase. Thus the beam peak appears at

$$\psi_p = \cos^{-1}(c/V_p) = \cos^{-1}(\sqrt{1 - (\lambda/2a)^2})^{-1} \qquad (4.8)$$

Since the direction of the beam peak is a function of λ, it is evident that considerable steering of the beam occurs as a function of frequency. In contrast with fast-wave structures, the directions of the beam maxima of many slow-wave structures are slowly variant with frequency.

As may be seen from Eq. 4.8, the leaky radiator peaks nearly end fire when λ is far from cutoff, and conversely approach broadside as the phase velocity approaches infinity.

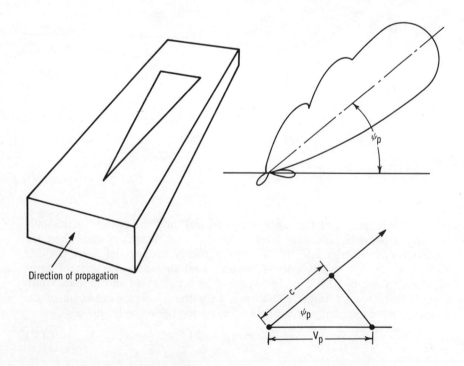

Direction of propagation

82. Slow-wave radiators

Another technique for forming slow-wave radiators involves the introduction of shaped metallic obstacles spaced periodically along a line. Simon and Weill have developed "cigar" antennas based upon metallic disk loading spaced periodically along a cylindrical rod. The reduction in propagation velocity along the antenna is enhanced as the disk diameter, D, is increased and as the spacing, s, is decreased.

In practice, both s/λ and D/λ range between about 0.2 to 0.4 whereas the velocity of propagation is slowed from about 5 to 25 per cent.

A second example of a slow-wave antenna based on the same principles as the cigar antenna is the Yagi—familiar as a directive TV or FM receiving antenna. The Yagi antenna consists of an array of coplanar conductive-rod elements, held at fixed spacings by an insulating post. Only one element, a half-wave dipole, is driven; the others are known as *parasitic elements.* (The half-wave dipole will be discussed in greater detail below.) The parasitic element in back of the dipole is called a *reflector;* those forward of the dipole are called *directors.* Since the reflector is slightly longer than $\lambda/2$, reradiation scattered by it suffers a phase advance of π radians. The reflector is spaced $\lambda/4$ behind the dipole so that its scattered energy will interfere constructively at the dipole.

Spacings of the director elements, s, typically lie between about 0.2λ and 0.4λ. The length of the director rods is chosen to be less than $\lambda/2$. A small phase retardation is thus introduced by each element, which decreases the velocity of propagation. Both the disks of the cigar antenna and the Yagi directors store reactive energy in their vicinity in the form of the higher order modes needed to satisfy E-field boundary conditions over the metallic obstacles.

CIGAR ANTENNA

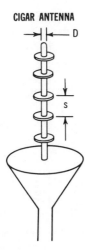

YAGI ANTENNA

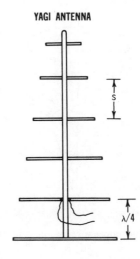

83. Very broad band radiators

High antenna gain is frequently achieved at the expense of bandwidth. The bandwidth of the Yagi antenna just described may be only a few per cent if its gain exceeds 10 db. By stagger-tuning the element lengths, it may be possible to achieve bandwidths of 50 per cent, but the resulting gain may drop 3 db or even more. The antennas next to be described are inherently moderate-gain antennas, but their element bandwidths are far in excess of other types. Four to five octaves—perhaps even more—are achievable. Careful arraying of these elements can result in high-gain, large-bandwidth antennas.

The so-called "frequency independent" antennas rely for broadband properties on designs that permit active radiation at a single frequency to occur over only a limited portion of the aperture. The structural size varies along the aperture. The active portion moves along the aperture, as the frequency changes, to a point at which the ratio of the physical dimension to λ is constant. Antennas designed by this concept are of either the equiangular or log-periodic types. Certain configurations of both types are characterized by a backward radiation mode, in which the radiated energy is directed toward the antenna's small, or feed, end.

The equiangular spiral antenna shown consists of a conductive wire or strip wound on a cone surface (strictly speaking, strip width should be increased linearly with distance from origin). A radius, r, from the cone apex to any spiral point intersects the spiral at a constant angle, ψ_0—hence the name, *equiangular*. Pencil beam patterns, circularly polarized, are obtained. They vary very little with frequency. Even the input impedance looking into the antenna terminals[1] varies slowly with frequency.

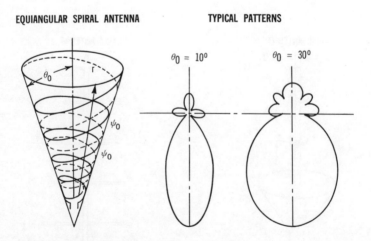

EQUIANGULAR SPIRAL ANTENNA   TYPICAL PATTERNS

$\theta_0 = 10°$ $\theta_0 = 30°$

[1] The impedance of the antenna circuit as measured at the antenna terminals.

84. Log-periodic antennas

The trapezoidal-tooth version of the log periodic clearly evidences the design principles involved in log-periodic antennas. Both anti-symmetric halves of the antenna may be regarded as variable-width transmission lines subtending the constant angle, ψ_0, at the source (for greatest bandwidth, the strip width should be proportional to its length as for the conical equiangular antenna). The transmission lines are loaded with conductive stubs whose lengths, l, widths, w, and distances from the center, r, bear a constant ratio, τ, to one another. The stubs extend variable lengths in such a way that their extremities subtend the constant angle, ψ_1, at the source. The frequency limits of operation range from $\lambda/4$, the shortest stub length, to $\lambda/4$, the longest.

The pattern of the trapezoidal antenna shown has two major lobes, pointing in opposite directions in a plane perpendicular to the paper. If the two halves of the antenna are folded toward each other, forming a shallow vee, a single-lobed, backward-radiation pattern is formed.

The log periodic dipole array shown has been derived from the trapezoidal antenna by making a 180° fold. It, too, has a single-lobed, backward-radiation pattern. Corresponding with the anti-symmetrical form of the trapezoidal antenna, the feed lines are reversed between successive dipole pairs. The constant-width dipoles, like the constant-width wire of the equiangular antenna, detract from the achievable bandwidth. Nevertheless, octave bandwidth performance is still possible.

LOG PERIODIC ANTENNAS

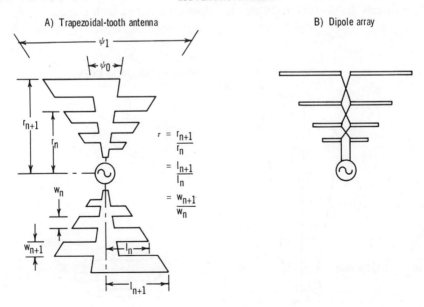

A) Trapezoidal-tooth antenna

B) Dipole array

$$\tau = \frac{r_{n+1}}{r_n}$$

$$= \frac{l_{n+1}}{l_n}$$

$$= \frac{w_{n+1}}{w_n}$$

85. Special horns

Although we have previously alluded to the application of horns as primary radiators, horns can be used as antennas in their own right. Pyramidal horns (flared in both planes, with flare angles limited to restrict aperture phase errors) are utilized as gain-standard antennas. The simple horn configuration permits a highly exact calculation of gain based solely upon aperture dimensions.

The gain-standard horn may be too long and heavy for other applications. It is possible to include a lens in the horn aperture to reduce its necessary length or to form shaped beams. The photograph shows a sectoral horn (flared in one plane only) with a variable-spacing metallic lens in its aperture for shaping the vertical plane pattern.

Another technique for achieving large gains with horns of moderate length is to terminate the horn with a section of a paraboloid, as shown in the figure. This type of antenna is known as a *hoghorn*. The high-gain hoghorn is characterized by very low backward lobe radiation. For a space communication system with low-noise maser amplifiers, it is important to employ antennas having very low backward radiation so as to discriminate against microwave noise generated by the temperature of the earth.

The cosine illumination in the *H* plane of a horn permits achievement of reasonably low side-lobe levels in this plane. In the *E* plane, however, high side lobes are to be expected for uniform aperture illumination. Brueckmann and Hagaman have circumvented this shortcoming by distorting the pyramidal horn to a pentagonal aperture shape, as shown in the figure for the TAHA antenna. The *E* lines, terminating normally upon the walls, are also distorted (so that an effective tapering is achieved). Low side-lobe levels (about 20 db) are thus achieved in both planes.

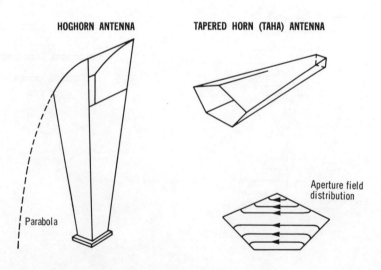

HOGHORN ANTENNA   TAPERED HORN (TAHA) ANTENNA

Parabola

Aperture field
distribution

SECTORAL HORN

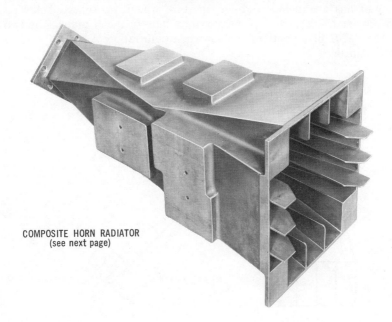

COMPOSITE HORN RADIATOR
(see next page)

86. Composite horn radiator

Proper illumination of the slant reflector of a dual V-beam antenna poses problems. The slant reflector is inclined 45° to the vertical, whereas its polarization is vertical. For low side lobes, primary illumination contours should parallel the reflector contour. Such illumination is achieved with a conventional pyramidal horn inclined by 45°, but its polarization will not be vertical. If it is vertical, the illumination will be unsatisfactory. How to resolve this problem?

To achieve proper illumination, it is mandatory to incline the horn aperture. The vertical edges of the horn serve as line-source generators about whose axes the pattern of the horn rotates in azimuth; the same is true of the horizontal edges. These axes must lie parallel to the plane of symmetry of the reflector for the contour lines to follow the reflector outline.

To obtain vertical polarization despite the aperture inclination, we resolve the E vector into two equal, orthogonal components. The horizontal, rectangular waveguide input to the horn is gradually distorted to a square, which is abruptly joined to another square rotated by 45°. This is then flared out in both planes to the desired aperture.

At the abutment, the E vector is decomposed into two equal, *cophasal,* orthogonal components. The radiated components are equal and rejoin in space along the horn axis to form a resultant vertical vector. But equality must be preserved for the two vector components over the entire reflector aperture. In short, the E-plane pattern of one component must match the H-plane pattern of the other, and vice-versa. This is achieved when sets of fins are included at the aperture which are spaced below cutoff, thereby restricting the E-plane aperture, but not the H-plane. The two sets of E- and H-plane patterns match when both ratios, AA′/BB′ = 3/2, are maintained.

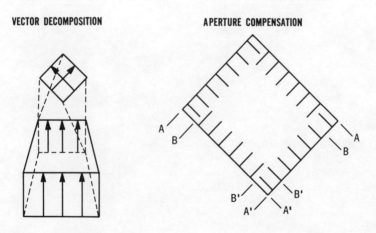

VECTOR DECOMPOSITION   APERTURE COMPENSATION

87. Small antennas

We have left to the last of this chapter a discussion of antennas that are small compared with wavelength. Included in this category are dipoles, slots, and loops. The patterns of all types of small antennas are essentially alike, except for polarization.

Structures that are small compared with wavelength are more difficult to treat mathematically than are large structures, to which geometric optics and scalar theory can be successfully applied. Mathematical treatises written on the subject of dipoles are concerned with an analytical description of the self and mutual impedances of dipoles. This book will limit itself to describing a few typical configurations and their associated characteristics.

The half-wave dipole consists of two collinear quarter-wave stubs. The half wavelength is a resonant structure, and reflections from its end points cause a standing wave to form across the antenna. The standing currents are in phase quadrature with the voltages across the antenna and store reactive energy in its vicinity. The tubes of force that span the antenna become detached as the standing waves reverse in sign and then radiate off into space.

The loss of energy to radiation is attributed to a radiation "resistance" across the transmission line. The radiation resistance of a thin half-wave dipole is about 70 ohms. This is a practical value comparable to that of the characteristic impedance of many transmission lines.[1] When the dipole is much shorter than a half-wavelength, its resistance drops to a few ohms or less. Complicated matching structures must then be devised to couple energy to the antenna.

HALF-WAVE DIPOLE ANTENNA

Standing wave

Tubes of force

Current distribution   Voltage distribution

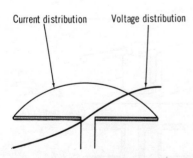
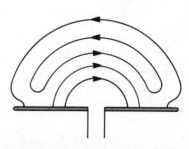

[1] See the next chapter for a discussion of the characteristic impedance of transmission lines and their proper termination for maximum power transfer.

88. Half-wave dipole

The pattern of a half-wave dipole very closely resembles that of the elementary dipole radiator (two isotropic, cophasal radiators spaced $\lambda/2$ apart). The patterns of both are doughnut-shaped, and the doughnut orientation is correct when the dipole axis threads the hole of the doughnut. The polarization of the pattern is such that the E vector is parallel to the dipole axis. Gain of the half-wave dipole is about 1.6 compared with 1.5 for the elementary dipole.

Equal excitation of the two wings of the dipole constitutes a common objective for the diverse forms of this radiator. This objective is readily met when circumstances permit a symmetrical excitation. A case in point is the dipole mounted on a metal plate that bifurcates the E plane of a rectangular waveguide. Such a situation arises in the splash-plate dipole feed shown in Fig. A. Other applications, however, may dictate an unbalanced feed, as in the case of a dipole coupled to a rectangular waveguide by a probe penetrating the broad face of the guide (Fig. B).

The degree of coupling of the dipole to the waveguide field may be increased by increasing the depth of penetration of the probe into the waveguide. The depth is usually kept shallow, for if it is increased too greatly, the probe itself will become resonant.

Since the broad face of the guide serves as a partial ground plane, an out-of-phase image is formed therein that increases the directivity of the pattern of a dipole supported a distance $\lambda/4$ above the ground plane. A quarter-wave slit (choke) in the coaxial feed of the dipole reflects an open circuit across the dipole terminals and helps to equalize the excitation of both wings.

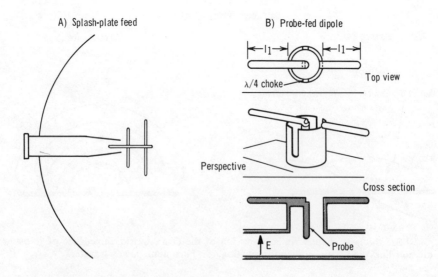

A) Splash-plate feed

B) Probe-fed dipole

$\lambda/4$ choke

Top view

Perspective

Cross section

E

Probe

89. Dipole-derived antennas

Modifications of the dipole have been evolved to satisfy special configuration, impedance, and bandwidth requirements. A vertical quarter-wave stub above a conductive ground plane finds much practical usage. Its pattern above the ground plane corresponds to that of the vertical dipole in the absence of the ground plane. At frequencies below the microwave range, quarter-wave lengths may be impractically long, in which case, as we have said, the radiation resistance may be so low that it is difficult to excite the antenna. It is possible to raise the radiation resistance of such antennas by end loading, that is, terminating the short stub by a horizontal conductive capacitor. Even at the higher frequencies, it is desirable to modify the dipole resistance in order to match a transmission line. The folded dipole shown in the figure has about four times the radiation resistance of the half-wave dipole. Its voltage is effectively doubled and its current halved. The folded dipole matches the impedance of a commercially available twin-lead transmission line.

One simple modification that increases the bandwidth of a half-wave dipole is to make the elements fat. Another is exemplified by the biconical and discone (disk-cone) antennas. The latter antennas, like the equiangular log periodics, attain their broadband characteristics by conserving angles. The low frequency cutoff is reached when each stub becomes less than $\lambda/4$ in length. If voltage standing-wave ratios of 2:1 are tolerable, the upper frequency limit may be two to three octaves above the lower cutoff frequency.

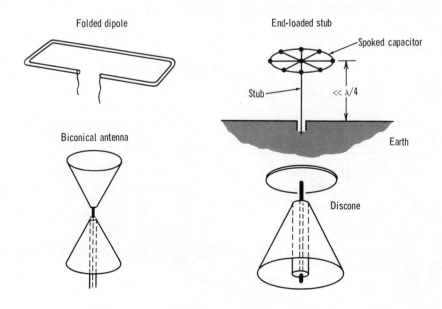

Folded dipole

End-loaded stub

Spoked capacitor

Stub

$\ll \lambda/4$

Earth

Biconical antenna

Discone

90. Slot radiators

A thin half-wave slot in an infinite conductive ground plane is "complementary" to a thin half-wave dipole in infinite free space. The patterns of the two are exactly alike except that the E and H vectors are interchanged. Whereas the dipole is excited by E fields parallel to the dipole axis, the E field of the slot is transverse. The E-field magnitude is sinusoidal along the slot, with its maximum at the center of the slot, and falls to zero at either end. For the dipole, the *currents* (which are associated with the H field) are sinusoidal along the axis, with a maximum at the center, whereas the *voltage* is zero at the center. Babinet first summarized the characteristics of complementary structures (Babinet's Principle) for scalar optics, but Booker extended the principle to include the polarization vectors.

In order to excite a slot, a component of the magnetic field must lie parallel to the slot. This component excites a current normal to the slot. Interruption of this current causes charges to build up on either side of the slot, and the E lines terminate the charges. Since the charges are short-circuited at either end of the slot, the E field must there fall to zero. As the direction of the exciting H field reverses, so does the sense of the E field across the slot. Radiation thus takes place by the mechanism previously described.

The perimeter of the slot when resonant approximately equals λ (as does the perimeter of the half-wave dipole). Whereas the impedance of the half-wave dipole approximates 70 ohms, that of the resonant slot is about 500 ohms. We have found that folding a half-wave dipole increases its radiation resistance fourfold. By complementarity, folding the resonant slot reduces its impedance to one-fourth its original value.

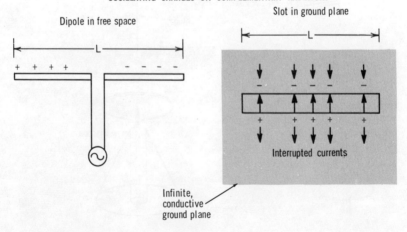

OSCILLATING CHARGES ON COMPLEMENTARY RADIATORS

Dipole in free space

Slot in ground plane

Interrupted currents

Infinite, conductive ground plane

91. Series slots in rectangular waveguide

Longitudinal currents, which proceed in the direction of propagation, are carried in the broad walls of the rectangular waveguide. These currents constitute the flow of charges terminating the E lines as they propagate down the length of the guide. Since the E lines terminate on charges of opposite sense on the top and bottom walls, the currents at any transverse section are 180° out of phase on the top and bottom walls. Hence the currents may be considered to flow down one face and return on the other.

Slots that interrupt the longitudinal currents are called series slots. The magnitude of the longitudinal currents transverse to the guide is cosinusoidal, following the transverse E-field magnitude. Therefore, the transverse series slot is excited with maximum intensity when the slot is centered with respect to the broad wall. Its magnitude may be reduced as $cos\,(\pi x/a)$ by displacing the center of the slot a distance x from the centerline.

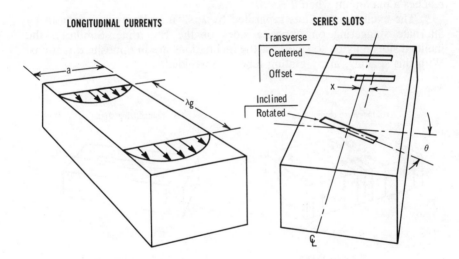

Alternatively, the centered slot may be rotated about its center (inclined) by an angle θ in order to diminish its coupling to the field in the guide. The inclined series slot coupling is not given by a simple expression, but it does diminish uniformly to zero when θ reaches 90°.

A slot array may be constructed by cutting slots at regular intervals along the length of the guide. A broadside array is formed when the interval just equals the waveguide wavelength, λ_g. All slots are then excited in phase. However, since λ_g for an air-filled guide exceeds λ, grating lobes will also be formed by the array unless special measures (such as loading the guide) are taken to avoid them. Shunt slots, next considered, avoid this shortcoming.

92. Shunt slots in rectangular waveguide

Shunt slots are slots that interrupt currents flowing transverse to the direction of propagation and that are associated with charges oscillating from the top to the bottom of a rectangular waveguide as the direction of the E field alternates with passage of the wave. The flow of transverse currents is shown in Fig. A; nonradiating slots are shown in Fig. B. Especially useful is the slot centered along the broad-face of the waveguide, for it offers a convenient entry point for the probe of interior fields along the direction of propagation.

The centered longitudinal slot may be caused to radiate by a parallel displacement off the centerline (Fig. C). Thus displaced, it interrupts shunt currents whose magnitude varies as $sin\ (\pi x/a)$, increasing from zero at the centerline to a maximum at the edge. The currents flow undiminished across the narrow face and return to the broad face. The inclined slot in the narrow face may be excited by orienting it at an angle θ so that it interrupts the shunt currents (Fig. D). This excitation is not a simple function but reaches a maximum when $\theta = 90°$.

The excitation of slots separated by $\lambda_g/2$ may be made cophasal by alternate staggering on opposite sides of the centerline. Similarly, the inclined slots may be so spaced if the inclinations are in opposite directions. With this spacing, array grating lobes are avoided.

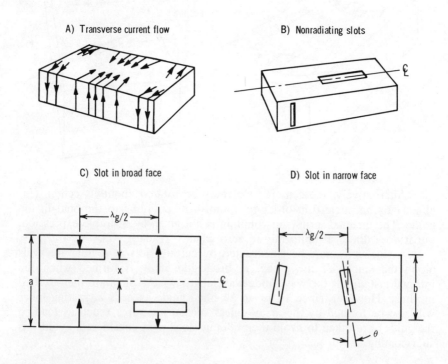

A) Transverse current flow

B) Nonradiating slots

C) Slot in broad face

D) Slot in narrow face

93. Loop antennas

The small-loop antenna is used principally as a radiator at the low end of the microwave spectrum. At higher frequencies it finds application as a coupler antenna inside a waveguide or cavity. A small loop is one whose circumference does not exceed one-fourth of a wavelength. Such an antenna has the typical doughnut-shaped "dipole" pattern. The loop is properly oriented with respect to the doughnut pattern when it serves as a hub lining the hole of the doughnut. In the case of the loop antenna, however, the *E* plane also contains the plane of the loop. In this restricted sense, then, the small-loop antenna is complementary to the short dipole and is known as a *magnetic dipole*.

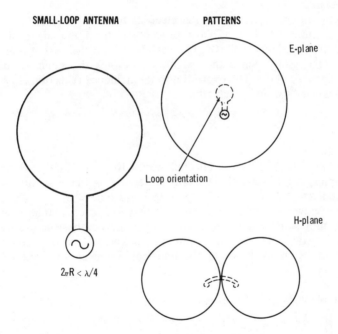

The small-loop antenna couples almost exclusively to the magnetic field (inductive coupling) and very little to the electric field (capacitive coupling). The *H* field threads through the center of the loop. As the circumference of the loop is reduced very much less than $\lambda/4$, its radiation resistance falls to a very low value (just as for the very short dipole). As the size of the loop is increased toward resonance, its radiation resistance increases. A still greater increase in the size of the loop will result in a variable resistance and the formation of a multi-lobed pattern. In these characteristics, its behavior is similar to that of the dipole when its stub length is increased beyond $\lambda/4$.

94. Radomes

A *radome* is a low-loss dielectric material used as an aperture seal for an antenna or as an entire enclosure around it. Its purpose may be the maintenance of internal pressurization or environmental protection. It can hardly be construed as a "type of antenna" but is discussed here because of its intimate association with many antennas.

Radomes are either electrically thin (A), half-wave (B), or sandwich (C) types. Thin radomes reflect little electromagnetic energy, even if a relatively high dielectric material is used. In Chapter 2 we found the reflection coefficient, ρ, for normal incidence to be

$$\rho = (n-1)/(n+1) \qquad (4.9)$$

Thus, at an air-dielectric interface for the modest value $\epsilon_r = 4.0$, we have the appreciable value, $\rho = 0.33$.

For the double interface of the electrically thin, lossless radome, the situation is different. For a wave proceeding from the air-to-dielectric interface, the angle of ρ is 180°. Conversely, at the dielectric-to-air interface, the angle is 0°. Since the magnitude of ρ is the same, destructive interference takes place. The over-all normal incidence reflection coefficient, R, is then given (approximately) by

$$R \cong \frac{4\pi\rho nt/\lambda}{1-\rho} \qquad (4.10)$$

where t is the wall thickness.

Cancellation of the two reflected waves from the half-wave radome (or multiples, N) is similar. The only difference is that the dielectric-air interface reflection travels a multiple of 360° further.

The sandwich radome consists of two (or more) relatively high dielectric, thin skins joined by a foam or honeycomb structure core of dielectric constant near unity. Minimum thickness depends both on the skin and core. Roughly, however, the skin separations approximate $\lambda/4$.

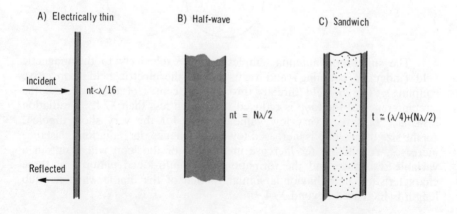

A) Electrically thin   B) Half-wave   C) Sandwich

Incident

$nt<\lambda/16$

$nt = N\lambda/2$

$t \cong (\lambda/4)+(N\lambda/2)$

Reflected

Summary of Chapter 4

The microwave art has borrowed the Cassegrain reflector directly from optics. Moreover, at microwave frequencies it is practical to use the properties of gratings to avoid sub-reflector blockage. Gratings also find application in dual polarization reflectors, Foster scanners, lightweight reflector mesh surfaces, and in other devices.

The Luneberg lens, its variants, and geodesic antennas—possessing circular symmetry—enjoy scanning properties independent of scan angle. Variations required in the index of refraction of Luneberg lenses can be achieved by synthesis utilizing both real and artificial dielectrics. Such dielectric media are also employed for surface wave, channel guide, leaky waveguide, cigar, and Yagi antennas.

Very broadband or frequency independent antennas may be constructed from an assemblage of interconnected radiating elements, progressively scaled in size and preserving critical angles. Radiation occurs from that portion of the aperture where the ratio of element size to wavelength is constant. These are the log-periodic and equiangular spiral antennas. They make effective broadband primary feeds. Other special feeds are the Taha, hoghorn, and composite feeds.

Radiators small compared with the wavelength—stubs, dipoles, slots, and loops—have similar doughnut-shaped radiation patterns. In fact, by the principle of complementarity, patterns of dipoles and slots are interchangeable. Antennas both large and small may be weatherized by enclosing them inside radomes that are transparent to microwaves.

Questions

1. Calculate the gain of a circular paraboloid of 20-in. radius operating at $\lambda = 3$ cm if (a) uniformly illuminated, (b) illuminated with a 10-db edge taper.

2. Estimate the peak side-lobe level for the above paraboloid when fed by a horn whose E and H-plane dimensions are 4 cm and 6 cm, respectively.

3. A Foster scanner, operating at $\lambda = 6$ cm, is 6 ft long and has a maximum mean rotor diameter of 18 in. and a minimum mean rotor diameter of 10 in. How many degrees can it steer its beam?

4. Plot the functional variation of (a) the dielectric constant, and (b) the index of refraction for a Luneberg lens.

5. Plot the index of refraction for the inner and outer circles of a small-circle Luneberg lens where r_o/R_o equals (a) 0.4, and (b) 0.6.

6. The dielectric constant of a linearly tapered surface wave beacon antenna is 4.0. If $\lambda = 10$ cm, what is its optimum radius? Assume that λ varies linearly with thickness and that the maximum thickness is at cutoff for the next higher hybrid mode.

7. Design a discone antenna capable of operating at 50 mc/sec.

8. A leaky waveguide radiator operates at $a/\lambda = 0.8$. At what angle with respect to the waveguide will the beam peak appear?

95. Introduction

Transmission line theory evolved long before the advent of microwave engineering. It provided a mathematical description for the transmission of low-frequency (such as 60-cycle) power over long distances from generator to consumer. Power-transmission lines deal with two cables separated by extremely small fractions of a wavelength. High power levels require balanced paired conductors a fixed distance apart whereas low power levels require either twinned pairs or coaxial lines. Fixed-separation pairs of wires (called Lecher wires) and coaxial cables are used up to the low-frequency end of the microwave spectrum. The theory of transmission lines applies directly to them.

At the higher frequency portion of the microwave spectrum, it becomes impractical to transmit power with two-wire lines because of the losses incurred. Therefore, hollow-pipe waveguides that have much lower losses are used. The hollow waveguides may be rectangular or circular in cross section or have one of the many special shapes to be discussed later in this chapter. Transmission line theory may be directly applied to waveguides provided that only one mode exists. Usually, it is possible to select the guide dimensions so that only the lowest order mode—the dominant mode— exists, the higher order modes being beyond cutoff. Sometimes it is possible to select one higher order mode for transmission in order to benefit from special properties—such as low loss or mode-configuration symmetries. In this event, utmost care must be taken not only to suppress lower order mode propagation, but also to avoid any discontinuities in the line.

Power engineering deals with the lumped-constant approach to transmission lines, in which the lines are composed of a network of resistances, capacitances, and inductances, and the variations in voltage and current are of concern. To apply these concepts to waveguides, the notion of distributed resistance, capacitance, and inductance must be introduced. Until now, we have concentrated attention solely on the electromagnetic fields, E and H. For transmission line theory, we should relate the two concepts.

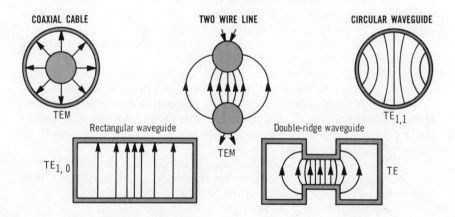

96. Voltage and current relationship to fields

At low frequencies, the voltage across a lumped constant or two-wire transmission line is well defined. The circuit elements are so small with respect to the wavelength that it is immaterial where the voltage is probed on the cross section of the wires. With careful measurement, a unique value of the voltage can be determined.

Consider now the problem of defining the voltage across a rectangular waveguide carrying energy in the $TE_{1,0}$ mode. No unique value can be obtained, for at any fixed cross section the y component of the electric field varies with the sending-end field, E_s, since

$$E_y = E_s \sin (\pi x/a) \tag{5.1}$$

over the cross section. Values from zero at the side walls to a maximum of E_s at $x = a/2$ are attained.

The voltage may be measured from top to bottom of the waveguide wall along any E line of the cross section. Since E_y is constant, the voltage is simply $V = (E_y) \ (b)$. It clearly depends upon which E_y line is chosen. The maximum value is $(E_s) \ (b)$. Consistency of application is all that is required.

Current is the second parameter spoken of at low frequencies, and its corresponding counterpart at microwave frequencies is the magnetic field. Similar remarks to those made concerning voltages and electric fields can be made concerning currents and magnetic fields. However, at microwave frequencies, a skin depth has to be defined to account for the fact that currents tend to flow near the surface of a conductor. We shall revert to this point later. At low frequencies, where magnetic field effects are small, the general practice relates current to the E field by the equation, $i = \sigma E$, and this notation is also followed at microwave frequencies (where the further effects of displacement currents are added). However, that this relation exists does not disprove our contention, since E cannot exist without H, and vice versa.

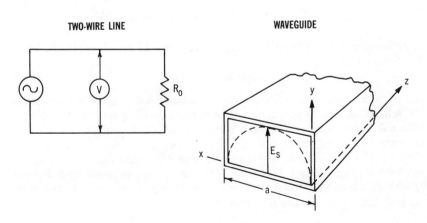

TWO-WIRE LINE   WAVEGUIDE

97. Transmission line equations — lossless lines

For a perfectly matched transmission line there is no reflected voltage or current. However, a general solution of the transmission-line equations requires both sending and reflected waves. Assuming a sinusoidal generator and no copper losses, the general solutions for voltage and current —each comprised of a sending and reflected wave—can be written as

$$V = V_s \cos \omega \left[t - (z/c) \right] + V_r \cos \omega \left[t + (z/c) \right] \qquad (5.2)$$

$$I = I_s \cos \omega \left[t - (z/c) \right] - I_r \cos \omega \left[t + (z/c) \right] \qquad (5.3)$$

Attention is directed to the sign differences in Eqs. 5.2 and 5.3. Within the cosine arguments, $[t - (z/c)]$ represents a positively going or sending wave, and $[t + (z/c)]$ a negatively going or reflected wave. The minus sign, prefixing the reflected current wave, follows the convention by which current flow opposite to the positive z direction is called negative. (The field counterpart of this we have previously discussed; namely, that upon reflection from a perfectly conductive surface, the sense of H, but not that of E, changes so that $E \times H$ changes in sign).

Suppose a generator to be connected to an infinitely long, lossless transmission line. The current that flows outward depends upon the generator voltage and upon the properties of the line, but in no way depends upon the load. The ratio of voltage to current is called the *surge impedance* or the *characteristic impedance, Z_0*, of the line. For a lossless line, Z_0 is purely resistive, hence $Z_0 = R_0$. For a lossless line either infinitely long or reflectionless, we have

$$Z_0 = R_0 = V_s/I_s = V/I \qquad (5.4)$$

A finite length of transmission line terminated by its characteristic impedance, R_0, will return no reflected wave and thus appear to a source to be infinitely long.

Equation 5-3, covering the general case admitting of reflections within the transmission line or at its termination, can be rewritten

$$I = \frac{V_s \cos \omega \left[t - (z/c) \right]}{R_0} - \frac{V_r \cos \omega \left[t + (z/c) \right]}{R_0} \qquad (5.5)$$

In arriving at Eq. 5-5 from Eq. 5-3, we have substituted $I_s = V_s/R_0$ from Eq. 5-4, and assumed that

$$Z_0 = R_0 = V_r/I_r \qquad (5.6)$$

just as if the line were reflectionless. In other words, in order to account for reflections, the concept of a steady-state sending and a steady-state reflected wave assumes, for each wave, an infinite length of transmission as if the line were reflectionless. The fact that $Z_0 = R_0$, a *real* number, means that V_s and I_s are in-phase with each other and that V_r and I_r are in-phase with each other. However, V_s is usually not in phase with V_r, nor I_s with I_r. Hence, the total voltage is usually not in phase with the total current, that is, V/I is usually complex.

98. Normalized impedance, reflection, and transmission coefficients

We shall now derive a few useful relationships that are of interest when discontinuities occur in a transmission line. Consider the simplest possible case—a uniform transmission line terminated by a mismatch impedance Z_L which differs from Z_0. It is conventional to measure distance backward from the load, which is located at $z = 0$. At the load, $V/I = Z_L$, and this ratio may be obtained by dividing Eq. 5.2 by Eq. 5.3, arbitrarily letting $t = 0$. Thus

$$Z_L = \frac{V_S + V_R}{I_S - I_R} \tag{5.7}$$

Substituting the values of Eqs. 5-4 and 5-6 into Eq. 5-7, we get

$$\frac{Z_L}{Z_0} = \frac{V_S + V_R}{V_S - V_R} \tag{5.8}$$

Defining the reflection coefficient, $\rho = V_R/V_S$, and substituting this into Eq. 5.8, we find both

$$\frac{Z_L}{Z_0} = \frac{1 + \rho}{1 - \rho} \tag{5.9}$$

and

$$\rho = \frac{Z_L - Z_0}{Z_L + Z_0} = \frac{(Z_L/Z_0) - 1}{(Z_L/Z_0) + 1} \tag{5.10}$$

The ratio Z_L/Z_0 is called the *normalized impedance,* ζ. For many transmission line problems, only this relative value of impedance is of concern, and hence ζ is loosely referred to as "the impedance." We shall also be guilty of this contraction below.

Defining the transmission coefficient, $\tau = V/V_s$, and substituting in Eq. 5.2 at the load, we get

$$\tau = 1 + \rho \tag{5.11}$$

Substituting this expression into Eq. 5.9, and again substituting for ρ, we derive

$$\tau = \frac{2Z_L}{Z_L + Z_0} = \frac{2\zeta}{1 + \zeta} \tag{5.12}$$

Defining VSWR as V maximum divided by V minimum, we get

$$\text{VSWR} = \frac{|V_S| + |V_R|}{|V_S| - |V_R|} \tag{5.13}$$

Equation 5.13 should be compared with Eq. 5.8, and all these should be compared with their counterparts derived for fields in Chapter 2.

99. Open circuit and short circuit — lossless lines

1. *Open circuit*—When a transmission line is open-circuited, the current at the load must fall to zero. Therefore, $I = I_s - I_R = 0$, or $I_s = I_R$. It also follows from Eq. 5.6 that $V_s = V_R$. Hence, at the load,

$$V = V_s + V_R = 2V_s \tag{5.14}$$
$$I = I_s - I_R = 0 \tag{5.15}$$

These relationships repeat every half-wavelength along a lossless line. One quarter wavelength back from the load

$$V = V_s + V_R = 0 \tag{5.16}$$
$$I = I_s - I_R = 2I_s \tag{5.17}$$

These relationships may be seen from the phasor diagrams below, remembering that sending and receiving vectors rotate in opposite directions. Each additional half-wavelength from the load, the relationships again repeat. The net voltage and net current are $90°$ apart in phase, indicating the delivery of zero power to the load.

2. *Short circuit*—No voltage can appear across a perfectly short-circuited termination. Hence $V_s = -V_R$, from which it follows that $I = 2I_s$. At the load

$$V = V_s + V_R = 0 \tag{5.18}$$
$$I = I_s - I_R = 2I_s \tag{5.19}$$

One-quarter wavelength from the load,

$$V = V_s + V_R = 2V_s \tag{5.20}$$
$$I = I_s - I_R = 0 \tag{5.21}$$

Thus, the short-circuit relationships are like those of the open circuit *except that the current and voltage vectors are interchanged.* On the other hand, it is not possible to deliver power to either an open- or short-circuited load; for both circuits, voltage and current are phased $90°$ apart everywhere along the line. Thus, even for a lossless line in which V_s/I_s and V_R/I_R are purely resistive (in phase), the ratio V/I is complex.

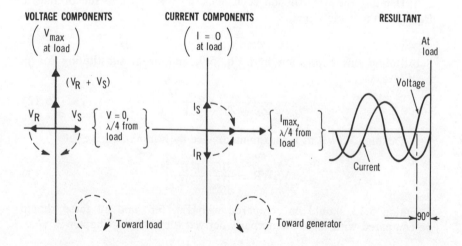

100. Resistive load — lossless lines

Suppose the transmission line to be terminated by a pure resistance, R, which differs from R_0, the characteristic impedance of the lossless line. Substituting in Eq. 5.10, we get for the reflection coefficient,

$$\rho = \frac{(R/R_0) - 1}{(R/R_0) + 1} \tag{5.22}$$

Since R and R_0 are both real, the expression for ρ is purely real, indicating that V_R and V_S are cophasal, and also I_R and I_S. The transmission coefficient, τ, is likewise real, and is given by

$$\tau = \frac{2R/R_0}{1 + (R/R_0)} \tag{5.23}$$

Both ρ and τ are plotted in the figure as functions of R/R_0. The short- and open-circuit cases previously described correspond with the values, $R/R_0 = 0$ and $R/R_0 = \infty$, respectively.

The power delivered to the load is I^2R. Since power is conserved, the power delivered to the load must equal the difference between sending and returning power:

$$I^2R = I_S^2R_0 - I_R^2R_0 \tag{5.24}$$

Dividing Eq. 5.24 by $I_S^2R_0$ yields the ratio of the power delivered to the load to the sending power and is given by

$$I^2R/I_S^2R_0 = 1 - (I_R/I_S)^2 = 1 - (V_R/V_S)^2$$

or
$$I^2R/I_S^2R_0 = 1 - \rho^2 \tag{5.25}$$

This is also plotted as a function of R/R_0. Notice that maximum power is delivered to the load when $R = R_0$.

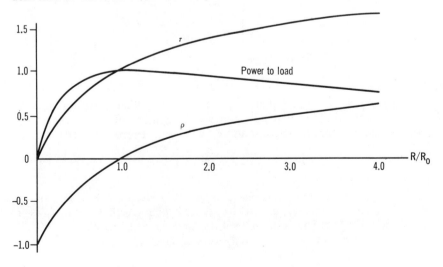

101. Reactive load — lossless lines

Energy is stored in the vicinity of a reactive load but not dissipated by it. For the purely inductive load, the resultant voltage leads the resultant current by 90° but lags it by 90° if the reactive load is capacitive.

An inductive load is written $+jX$ and a capacitive load $-jX$, in which X is the reactance, a real number. *At the load,* a short-circuited transmission line is inductive, whereas an open-circuited line is capacitive. These relationships apply not only at the load but also within a quarter wavelength thereof. Since V and I are 90° apart in phase, either the voltage or current, hence Z, changes sign every quarter wavelength from the load. Thus the line is alternately inductive or capacitive. As we shall see, this characteristic is important to impedance matching.

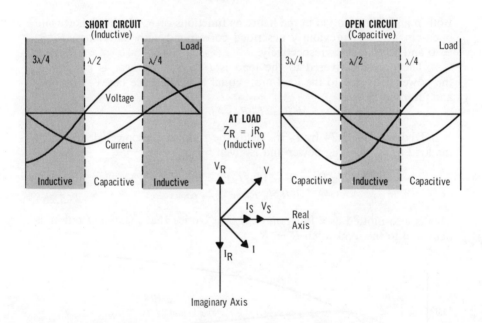

If the reactive load equals $+jX$ and X is neither zero nor infinity, the phase relationships depend upon the magnitude of X. Consider the specific case for the inductive load, $Z_L = +jR_0$. From Eq. 5.10, we get

$$\rho = \frac{j-1}{j+1} = j \qquad (5.26)$$

whose magnitude is unity and phase angle, 90°. Hence, $V_R = jV_s$, or V_R leads V_s by 90°. Since Z_0 is resistive, I_s is in phase with V_s, and I_R is in antiphase with V_R. The resultant voltage and current are likewise 90° in phase, therefore, indicating no dissipation of energy.

102. Complex load — lossless lines

By definition, a complex load is composed of both resistive and reactive components. For a complex load, we write

$$Z_L = R + jX \tag{5.27}$$

whose magnitude and phase angle, respectively, are given by

$$|Z_L| = \sqrt{R^2 + X^2} \tag{5.28}$$

$$tan\ \phi = X/R \tag{5.29}$$

Since neither X nor R is zero, Eq. 5.29 reveals that ϕ can be neither 90° nor 0° and that some energy is thus dissipated by a complex load.

Obviously a wide range in values of R and X is possible. To illustrate the method for handling complex loads, consider the special case when $Z_L = R_0\ (1 + j)$. The resistance and reactance are both equal to the characteristic impedance. From Eq. 5.29 we get $tan\ \phi = 1$, $\phi = 45°$, so that V leads I by 45°. For the reflection coefficient we have

$$\rho = \frac{1 + j - 1}{1 + j + 1} = \frac{j}{2 + j} = \frac{1 + 2j}{5} \tag{5.30}$$

The phase angle of ρ, or V_R/V_S, is thus $tan^{-1}(2) \cong 63°$ and its magnitude, $\sqrt{5}/5$. The magnitude and phase of V/V_S are given by Eq. 5.11, whence

$$\tau = (6 + 2j)/5 \tag{5.31}$$

whose phase angle is $tan^{-1}\ (1/3)$ or $\cong 18°$. With this information, the phasor relationships at the load can be constructed as shown in the figure. The power dissipated in the load is given by

$$P = VI \cos 45° \tag{5.32}$$

RELATIONSHIPS AT LOAD

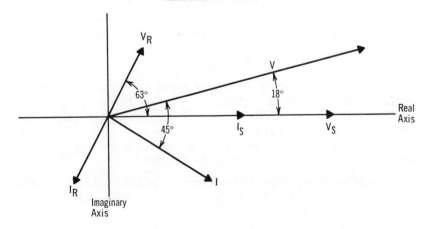

103. Impedance along lossless transmission line

The impedance looking toward the load may be found at any point along the line once the current and voltage relationships at the load are known. By superposition, sending and returning voltage and current waves may be added separately at any position along the line to determine the ratio of the net voltage to the current Z. When the line is lossless, these values are cyclically repetitive down the line. Thus, one can start with Eqs. 5.2 and 5.3, account for phase as well as amplitude relationships between V_s and V_r and between I_s and I_r, separately determine V and I, and finally take their ratio to establish $Z(z)$ at an arbitrary distance, $z = 1$, from the load. After some algebraic manipulations, which are somewhat tedious to perform, one derives alternative values for Z at any position z from the load:

$$Z(z) = Z_0 \frac{Z_L \cos \beta z + jZ_0 \sin \beta z}{Z_0 \cos \beta z + jZ_L \sin \beta z} \tag{5.33}$$

$$Z(z) = Z_0 \frac{Z_L + jZ_0 \tan \beta z}{Z_0 + jZ_L \tan \beta z} \tag{5.34}$$

where $\beta = 2\pi/\lambda g$ and λg is the wavelength of the transmission line.

Another useful relation is the value of ρ measured at a distance z from the load. This is given by

$$\rho(z) = \rho e^{j2\beta z} \tag{5.35}$$

The magnitude of ρ does not vary as a function of z, as may be seen, since $|e^{j2\beta z}| = 1.0$. The phase constant of ρ, $2\beta z$, varies at twice the rate of either sending or returning waves, since the waves are traveling toward each other. Thus the phase of ρ rotates $360°$ each half wavelength along the line. As ρ rotates one cycle, it is twice real—when V_S and V_R are in phase and when they are in anti-phase. Probing the voltage at these points along the line measures the voltage standing wave ratio,[1] σ. From Eq. 5.13,

$$\sigma = \frac{|V_s| + |V_R|}{|V_s| - |V_R|} = \frac{1 + |\rho|}{1 - |\rho|} \tag{5.36}$$

Manipulating Eq. 5.36, we also get the reciprocal relationship

$$|\rho| = \frac{\sigma - 1}{\sigma + 1} \tag{5.37}$$

An impedance meter is utilized to probe for voltage maxima and minima. It will be described in greater detail in the chapter on microwave components. Briefly, it consists of an electrically short stub carried on a precision carriage along the length of the transmission line. In a waveguide, the stub penetrates a short distance into the guide through a nonradiating longitudinal slot centered in the broadwall.

[1] Some British authors define VSWR as the reciprocal of Eq. 5-36. Thus VSWR is a fraction, equal to or less than unity, whereas in our notation it equals or is larger than unity.

104. Impedance — special cases

Treating a few special cases of Eq. 5.33 may be helpful in revealing its application. Some we have already considered.

1. Let $Z_L = Z_0$. Then,

$$Z(z) = Z_0 \left(\frac{Z_0 \ (cos \ \beta z + sin \ \beta z)}{Z_0 \ (cos \ \beta z + sin \ \beta z)} \right) = Z_0 \qquad (5.38)$$

or, the impedance of a line terminated by Z_0 is Z_0.

2. Let $Z_L = 0$. Then,

$$Z(z) = Z_0 \ (jZ_0 \ tan \ \beta z / Z_0) = jZ_0 \ tan \ \beta z \qquad (5.39)$$

or, the short-circuited line is purely reactive and is inductive at the load $(z = 0)$.

3. Let $Z_L = \infty$. First dividing numerator and denominator of Eq. 5.33 by Z_L, we get

$$Z(z) = Z_0 \ (1/j \ tan \ \beta z) = -jZ_0 \ cot \ \beta z \qquad (5.40)$$

or, the open-circuited line is purely reactive and is capacitive at the load. Equations 5.39 and 5.40 are sketched in the figure.

Let Z_{sc} and Z_{oc} be the sending-end impedances of the short-circuited and open-circuited lines. From Eqs. 5.39 and 5.40 we have

$$(Z_{sc}) (Z_{oc}) = \frac{jZ_0 \ tan \ \beta z}{j \ tan \ \beta z / Z_0} = Z_0{}^2$$

$$Z_0 = \sqrt{(Z_{sc}) (Z_{oc})} \qquad (5.41)$$

$$\frac{Z_{sc}}{Z_{oc}} = \frac{jZ_0 \ tan \ \beta z}{-jZ_0 \ cot \ \beta z} = -tan^2 \ \beta z$$

$$tan \ \beta z = \sqrt{-Z_{sc}/Z_{oc}} \qquad (5.42)$$

Thus by measuring the impedance of the lossless transmission line, both open-circuited and short-circuited, the characteristic impedance and the distance from the load may be determined.

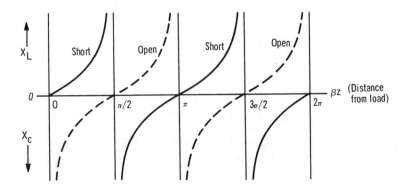

105. Impedance matching — lossless line

Standing waves will be set up by reflections from any discontinuity within a transmission line. Wherever the mismatch—whether at the load or elsewhere—the transfer of power to the load may be maximized by the deliberate introduction of a compensating discontinuity so that the introduced reflected wave will interfere destructively with that from the mismatch. A standing wave will then remain only between the two mismatches —storing reactive power. This situation is illustrated in the figure.

A few specific examples may be helpful in illustrating the concepts.

1. *Quarter wavelength transformer (Case I)*—Suppose a transmission line to be terminated by a resistive load, R, that is different from the characteristic impedance. The sending impedance a quarter wavelength from the load is

$$Z_s = Z\,(\lambda/4) = Z_0^2/R = R_0^2/R \qquad (5.43)$$

Z_s is thus a pure resistance, either larger or smaller than R_0 as R is smaller or larger, respectively, than R_0. If the transmission line impedance between where Z_s was measured and the generator is equal to R_0^2/R, the entire line is matched to the load. Therefore, a transmission line a quarter wavelength long can match two resistive impedances if its characteristic resistance $R_0 = \sqrt{(R)(R_s)}$.

2. *Half-wavelength transformer (Case II)*—Substituting $\beta z = \pi$ in Eq. 5.33 we get

$$Z\,(\lambda/2) = Z_0\,(Z_L/Z_0) = Z_L \qquad (5.44)$$

Thus at the input to a half-wavelength line, the impedance is the same as at its output, *regardless of* Z_0. For example, if Z_R is the impedance of space, a half wavelength of uniform dielectric will match an oncoming wave. This is the principle of the half-wavelength radome previously studied.

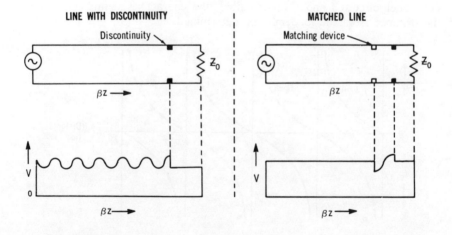

105. Impedance matching — lossless line (Cont.)

3. *Reactive matching devices* (*Case III*)—Impedance matching devices, such as the transformers just discussed, are in series with the transmission line.Odd lengthsof transmission line, in series, may also be used as impedance-matching devices, since both real and imaginary values of impedance are transformed by line lengths in accordance with Eq. 5.33. Whereas line lengths are useful matching devices, they are not as frequently used as reactive discontinuities for this purpose. The latter, shown in the figure, are conductive obstacles whose linear extent along the transmission line is small compared with a quarter wavelength.

All the obstacles shown are shunted across the waveguide. The net impedance at the point of insertion is the parallel impedance, Z_p, which is presented by the obstacle discontinuity, Z_D, and the load impedance transformed by the line length from the load, Z_T:

$$Z_p = (Z_T)(Z_D)/(Z_T + Z_D) \qquad (5.45)$$

The objective is to choose the proper value of $\beta 1$ and Z_D, so that $Z_p = Z_0$. In terms of Eq. 5.33, the problem is somewhat messy. It is much simpler when handling matching problems with shunt elements to deal with admittances. By the same token, when matching with series elements— as for cases I and II—the proper choice is the impedance equation.

It therefore behooves us to discuss the admittance equation. Furthermore, since both impedance and admittance problems are most readily handled using the Smith chart, we shall describe this chart briefly. Then we shall return to the problem of matching with reactive discontinuities.

WAVEGUIDE REACTIVE OBSTACLES

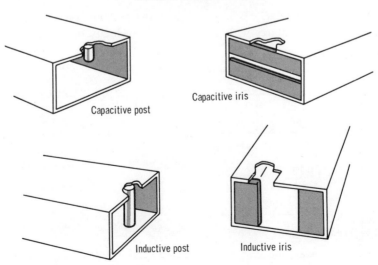

Capacitive post

Capacitive iris

Inductive post

Inductive iris

106. Representations of the line

The transmission line supporting only one mode of propagation may be represented by a series inductance and resistance per unit length and a shunt capacitance and conductance per unit length. Conductance, G, is the reciprocal of resistance. Zero conductance indicates an open resistance across the line. For the lossless line, therefore, both the series resistance and shunt conductance are zero.

The line may be described either in terms of its series impedances, which are additive,

$$Z = R + jL\omega \qquad (5.46)$$

or in terms of its shunt admittances, Y, which are likewise additive,

$$Y = G + jC\omega \qquad (5.47)$$

The characteristic impedance of the line is given by

$$Z_0 = \sqrt{\frac{R + j\omega L}{G + j\omega C}} \qquad (5.48)$$

or the characteristic admittance

$$Y_0 = \sqrt{\frac{G + j\omega C}{R + j\omega L}} \qquad (5.49)$$

If both R and G are zero, then the characteristic impedance reduces to $\sqrt{L/C}$, which compares with $\sqrt{\mu/\epsilon}$ for the impedance of waves in space.

The propagation constant of the line is defined as $\gamma = \alpha + j\beta$, where β is the phase constant with which we have been dealing and α is an attenuation factor for the lossy line. The propagation constant is

$$\gamma = \sqrt{ZY} = \sqrt{(R + j\omega L)\,(G + j\omega C)} \qquad (5.50)$$

For the lossless line, $\beta = \omega\,\sqrt{LC}$, and the velocity of propagation is $1/\sqrt{LC}$, which compares with $1/\sqrt{\mu\epsilon}$ for the velocity of waves in space.

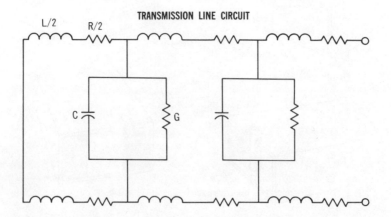

TRANSMISSION LINE CIRCUIT

107. Admittance relationships

From the similarity of Eqs. 5.46 and 5.47, one would expect that all previous relationships derived in terms of impedances would have their counterpart expressions in terms of admittances, and, indeed, the parallelism is nearly perfect. We have for the voltage reflection coefficient,

$$\rho = \frac{Y_0 - Y_L}{Y_0 + Y_L} = \frac{1 - (Y_L/Y_0)}{1 + (Y_L/Y_0)} \tag{5.51}$$

and for the transmission coefficient,

$$\tau = \frac{2Y_0}{Y_0 + Y_L} = \frac{2}{1 + (Y_L/Y_0)} \tag{5.52}$$

Comparing these equations with their equivalents, Eqs. 5.10 and 5.12, it is seen that the subscripts are interchanged. Completing our parallelism, we write the counterpart of Eqs. 5.33 and 5.34, thus,

$$Y(z) = Y_0 \left(\frac{Y_L \cos \beta z + jY_0 \sin \beta z}{Y_0 \cos \beta + jY_L \sin \beta z} \right) \tag{5.53}$$

and

$$Y(z) = Y_0 \left(\frac{Y_L + jY_0 \tan \beta z}{Y_0 + jY_L \tan \beta z} \right) \tag{5.54}$$

Comparing these equations with their counterparts, it is seen that the subscripts are identical. If charts are made up relating the impedance and admittance transformation equations, one would think that their usage would be identical. And so it can be, with proper definitions of signs.

Letting $Z = 1/Y$, in which $Z = R + jX$ and $Y = G + jB$ (B is called the *susceptance*), we have

$$R + jX = \frac{1}{G + jB} = \left(\frac{G}{G^2 + B^2} \right) - j \left(\frac{B}{G^2 + B^2} \right) \tag{5.55}$$

For equality, both real and imaginary parts must be equal. Therefore, it would appear that a *positive* reactance corresponds with a *negative* susceptance, and vice versa. Some authors adopt this convention. When they do, the direction of travel, toward or away from the load, is the *same* in charts for impedance or admittance. Other authors call an inductive susceptance positive, corresponding with a positive inductive reactance. Similarly, they call capacitive reactances or susceptances negative. When this convention is adopted, the direction of travel is *opposite* for impedance and admittance. We shall adopt the former convention.

108. Pair of matched posts

We shall now demonstrate the use of the admittance formulas by solving the following problem. Suppose it is desired to increase the electrical length of a matched transmission line reactively without reflecting any energy back toward the generator. This is impossible unless at least two spaced reactive discontinuities are used. We shall use a pair of capacitive posts or screws, equalizing their depth of insertion and properly selecting their separation. Place the first screw, of susceptance jB, nearest the load. Since the transmission line is assumed to be matched, at every position of insertion the normalized admittance is, $Y = 1 + jB$ Incidentally, for the rest of this discussion, the matching problem is precisely that of Case III (reactive matching devices).

Further, since the second screw will also add susceptance, jB, at its point of insertion, the transformed admittance of the first screw must be $1.0 - jB$, so that the net admittance at that point is $Y(z) = 1.0 - jB + jB = 1.0$, a match. Therefore, substituting in Eq. 5.54, we get

$$1 - jB = \frac{1 + jB + j \tan \beta z}{1 + j \tan \beta z \, (1 + jB)} \qquad (5.56)$$

With a little algebraic manipulation, and by equating real and imaginary components of Eq. 5.56, we arrive at the proper separation.

$$\tan \beta z = 2/B \qquad (5.57)$$

This solution is precisely analogous to that of selecting the proper separation for a sandwich radome.

Also, from Eq. 5.51, we derive

$$\rho = \frac{1 - 1 - jB}{1 + 1 + jB} = \frac{-jB}{2 + jB} \qquad (5.58)$$

so that the absolute value of ρ is

$$|\rho| = B/(B^2 + 4)^{1/2} \qquad (5.59)$$

and its phase angle is

$$\angle \rho = -90° - \tan^{-1} B/2 \qquad (5.60)$$

Similarly, for τ, we derive

$$|\tau| = 2/(B^2 + 4)^{1/2} \qquad (5.61)$$

and

$$\angle \tau = -\tan^{-1} B/2 \qquad (5.62)$$

The angle of τ is the insertion phase of each screw, and hence the total insertion phase is: $\Delta \phi = -2 \tan^{-1} B/2$.

We shall next describe the solution for this very same problem using the Smith chart so that a direct comparison may be made.

109. Basis of the Smith chart

The magnitude of the reflection coefficient does not vary as a function of position along the lossless transmission line. Since V_R and V_S represent waves traveling in opposite directions, the time average of their ratio must be independent of position along the line. The relative phase of V_R and V_S, however, *does* depend upon position and, since they travel in opposite directions, changes at twice the rate of either. Hence,

$$\rho(z) = \rho e^{j2\beta z} \qquad (5.63)$$

where ρ is the value (magnitude and phase) at the load. Since the magnitude of $e^{j2\beta z}$ is always unity, $\rho(z)$ traces out a circle of 360° every time the line length increases by 180°. All possible magnitudes of ρ lie between 0.0 and 1.0. Hence, if impedance or admittance values are associated with each terminal point of ρ, all possible values can be plotted within a circle of unit radius. The Smith chart makes this association, using normalized values. The center of this circle corresponds with the value, $Y_0 = Z_0 = 1 + j0$, or a perfectly matched transmission line. Whenever $\angle\rho = 0$ or 180°, the load is purely real, that is, resistive. It follows that all real impedance or admittance values lie on a diameter. The point 1,0 ($R = 1.0$, $x = 0$) lies at the center.

The real axis is usually shown as the horizontal diameter, with $R = 0$ to the left and $R = \infty$ to the right. Obviously, ρ crosses the real axis twice per revolution. The right-hand crossing corresponds with an in-phase condition for V_S and V_R, and the left-hand crossing with an anti-phase condition. The VSWR value can be read at the right-hand intercept. A clockwise rotation of ρ corresponds with rotation toward the generator and a counterclockwise rotation with rotation toward the load.

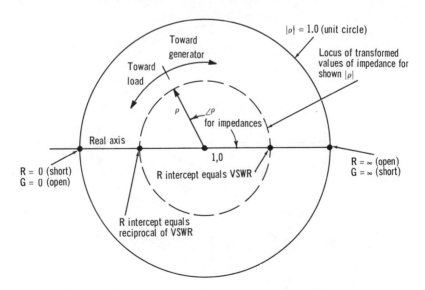

110. The Smith chart

Electrical distance is indicated along the periphery of the unit circle of the Smith chart. Units of distance, corresponding with the angle of ρ, are in terms of wavelengths. Usually, two scales are shown, with origins at opposite ends of the real axis. The two origins correspond with impedance and admittance voltage minima (with a short circuit, at $R = 0$ and $G = \infty$). The voltage minimum is located with an impedance meter.

Transformed impedance values are to be read at the terminal point of ρ as it traces out a circle centered on 1,0. At every terminal point, the desired values correspond with the values of two intersecting circles (actual or interpolated). Normalized values of resistance (or conductance) form one set, and normalized values of reactance (susceptance) form the other set. The two sets intersect orthogonally (at right angles) as shown. The set of constant resistance circles are all tangent to the real axis at $R = \infty$, whereas the set of constant reactance circles all pass through $R = \infty$ but cross the real axis at right angles.

By our previous sign convention, positive reactances (inductive) and susceptances (capacitive) are plotted above the real axis. Similarly, capacitive reactances and inductive susceptances—both negative—are plotted below. With this usage, the plotted point, $0.4 + j\,(1.0)$, represents either $Z = R + jX$ or $Y = G + jB$, as required. The use of the chart is then identical for both cases. The *only* differences, then, are in reading the angle of ρ and the location of the origin of the τ vector.

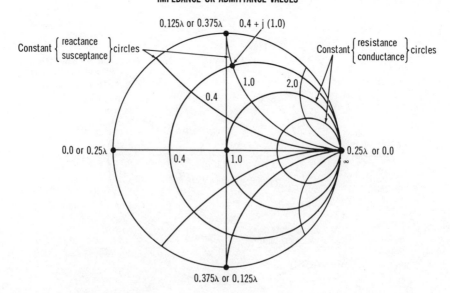

IMPEDANCE OR ADMITTANCE VALUES

111. Pair of matched posts — Smith chart solution

The angle of ρ equals $0°$ for an open and $180°$ for a short. But short and open locations are at opposite ends of the real axis when we deal with impedances and admittances. Hence, the angles of ρ for impedances and admittances are supplementary. Furthermore, since $\tau = 1 + \rho$ whether the impedance or admittance notation is in use, the origin of τ is located at opposite ends of the real axis. These relationships are summarized in Fig. A.

In Fig. B, we proceed to solve the matched post problem. These are twin capacitive screws, inserted equal depths so that $B = 1.0$, resulting in a phase shift but no mismatch. Since the transmission line was presumed terminated in its characteristic admittance, the chart may be entered at 1,0 (point 1). The shunt susceptance of the first screw is added by proceeding along the circle, $G = 1.0$, to the intersection, $B = 1.0$ (point 2). ρ may now be drawn from 1,0 to this intersection and then rotated toward the generator until the circle, $G = 1.0$, is again intersected (point 3). The positive susceptance of the second screw is added by proceeding upward along $G = 1.0$ by an amount $B = 1.0$. This restores the admittance to the value, $1 + j0$, at point 1.

It is left to the reader to calculate the values of ρ and τ at points 2 and 3. The angle values may be read off the chart itself, provided that the electrical lengths around the chart are converted to geometric values by multiplying by a factor of two.

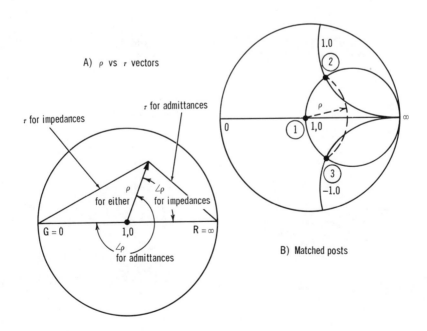

A) ρ vs τ vectors

τ for admittances

τ for impedances

ρ for either

$\angle\rho$ for impedances

$G = 0$ 1,0 $R = \infty$

$\angle\rho$ for admittances

B) Matched posts

112. Lossy lines

The reader might well ask why we have built an extensive theory on the assumption of a lossless transmission line when, in reality, no such line exists. The answer is twofold: (1) Many transmission line characteristics are well represented by the lossless assumption since it is a good one, and (2) the assumption helps to simplify the equations. In many practical cases where attenuation cannot be ignored, the starting point of analysis involves an assumption of no loss, and results are then modified by a knowledge of the effects of attenuation.

The periodicity of standing waves in a transmission line is but little affected by small losses. There is a small periodic reduction or decrement in the VSWR in the direction of the generator that is caused both by the losses in the forward and the reverse waves. The figure shows an exaggeration of the effect, which, however, does decay exponentially.

The forward-wave amplitude and phase vary as $e^{\gamma l} = e^{(\alpha + j\beta)l}$, and the reverse wave as $e^{-(\alpha + j\beta)l}$. In both instances, l is measured from the load. For the low-loss line, β is much greater than α.

We have the identity, $e^{(\alpha + j\beta)l} \equiv (e^{\alpha l})(e^{j\beta l})$. Since $|e^{j\beta l}| = 1.0$, the factor, $e^{\alpha l}$, accounts for an exponential increase of the sending wave in the direction of the generator. Similarly, $e^{-\alpha l} = 1/e^{\alpha l}$ accounts for an exponential decrease of the reverse wave in the generator direction. The reflection coefficient (their ratio) therefore varies as

$$\rho(l) = \frac{e^{-(\alpha l + j\beta l)}}{e^{\alpha l + j\beta l}} = e^{-2(\alpha l + j\beta l)}$$

$$= (e^{j2\beta l})(e^{-2\alpha l}) \tag{5.64}$$

Thus, as βl increases in the direction toward the generator on a Smith chart, ρ spirals inward, as shown (exaggeratedly) in the figure.

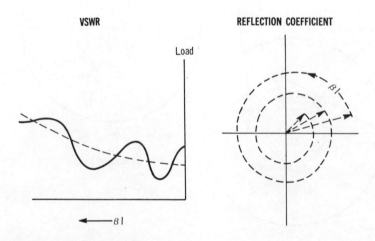

VSWR   REFLECTION COEFFICIENT

113. Skin effect

The depth of penetration of alternating currents into metals decreases exponentially away from the surface of metal exposed to the exciting field. At frequencies in the megacycle range, nearly all the current is carried in a thin skin near the surface. If J_s is the current density at the surface, current density at a depth x below the surface is

$$J(x) = J_s e^{-x/\delta} \tag{5.65}$$

When $x = \delta$, the "penetration depth," the current has fallen to a value $1/e$ times that at the surface (about 37 per cent). It has been shown that the penetration depth is given by the formula

$$\delta = 1/\sqrt{\pi \mu f \sigma} \text{ meters} \tag{5.66}$$

where μ is the permeability, f the frequency in cycles per second, and σ the conductivity in mhos per meter. For nonferromagnetic media, we have

$$\delta = (5.034)(10^2)/\sqrt{f\sigma} \text{ meters} \tag{5.67}$$

An equivalent resistance for high frequencies may be defined. In general, this differs from the direct-current resistance of metal, except for the semi-infinite plane conductor, where the two are equal. The equivalent resistance is taken as the resistance of a square area by a thickness of δ through which a *uniform* current flows, where the current value is chosen as half that at the surface.

Since the value of δ at microwave frequencies is in the order of thousandths of an inch, or less, it is obvious that surface roughness can drastically affect conductivity. Surface finishes of a precision in the order of tens of microinches are sometimes desirable.

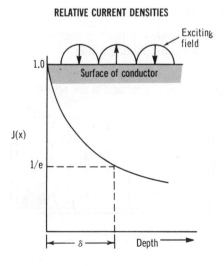

RELATIVE CURRENT DENSITIES

CONDUCTIVITIES OF METALS
(mhos per meter)

Silver	6.3×10^7
Copper	5.8×10^7
Gold	4.1×10^7
Aluminum	3.5×10^7
Brass	1.4×10^7
Nickel	1.2×10^7

114. Power handling capacity

Transmission lines are limited in the amount of power they are capable of handling both by average-power and peak-power considerations. Limitations on average power result from conductor or dielectric losses that appear as heat and may ultimately result in material failure. Such affects may be mitigated by cooling the walls of the transmission line.

Peak power limitations are imposed as the result of dielectric breakdown and conduction when the voltage gradient becomes sufficiently great. For a standard atmosphere of dry air devoid of free ions or electrons, this occurs at a gradient of 30,000 volts per centimeter. In actual practice a more modest value is acceptable—perhaps 20,000 volts per centimeter.

Whatever a line's power-handling capacity, it is reduced by obstacles placed within the line. Right at the obstacle, the maximum allowable gradient is reduced and a reflected wave set up that adds to the oncoming wave and limits the peak amount of transmitted power.

Let P_0 equal the maximum amount of power capable of being handled by a matched transmission line. The corresponding maximum voltage is V_m, where $P_0 Z_0 = V_m^2$. This maximum voltage cannot be exceeded when the line is mismatched, so we may write, $V_M = V_s + V_R$. Therefore

$$V_s = V_m - V_R$$
$$= V_m - \rho V_s \tag{5.68}$$

or
$$V_s = V_m/(1+\rho) = \sqrt{P_0 Z_0}/(1+\rho)$$

Thus, the new, maximum sending power in the presence of a reflected wave is

$$V_s^2/Z_0 = P_0/(1+\rho)^2 \tag{5.69}$$

In terms of the voltage standing wave ratio, σ, Eq. 5.69 may be written

$$V_s^2/Z_0 = P_0\,(\sigma + 1/2\sigma)^2 \tag{5.70}$$

Thus, for example, if the VSWR = 2.0, the peak power capacity of the transmission line is only 9/16 of the same matched line.

OBSTACLE IN HIGH FIELD REGION   OBSTACLE IN LOW FIELD REGION

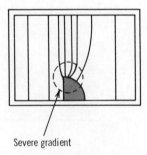

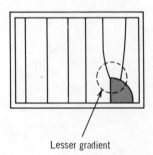

Severe gradient   Lesser gradient

115. Two-wire line and coaxial line

Previously we have alluded to the two-wire line. Presuming the two conductors to be circular in cross section, each of radius r, and with center-to-center separation, s, the characteristic impedance is

$$Z_0 = (276/\sqrt{\epsilon_r}) \log s/r \text{ ohms} \tag{5.71}$$

Of course, for an open-wire line embedded in no dielectric, $\epsilon_r = 1.0$.

The coaxial line propagates energy in the annular space between the inner conductor and the concentric outer conductor, both circular in cross section. If the radius of the inner conductor is r and that of the outer, R, we have, for the TEM mode,

$$Z_0 = (138/\sqrt{\epsilon_r}) \log R/r \tag{5.72}$$

where $\epsilon_r = 1.0$ if the annular space is air-filled.

The attenuation of a wave along a transmission line, as we have seen, is given by e^{-al}. When $al = 1.0$, the signal strength has fallen to $1/e$ times its value. The attenuation constant, α, is then expressed in nepers per meter. The constant, α, in terms of decibels per meter, is equal to some 8.69 times α expressed in nepers. Attenuation is comprised of the sum of conductor losses and of dielectric losses. For the conductor losses of a TEM wave in a coaxial line, we have

$$\alpha_c = \frac{5.9}{R\lambda_m} \left(\frac{1}{R} + \frac{1}{r} \right) \frac{\sqrt{\epsilon_r}}{\log R/r} \text{ decibels per meter} \tag{5.73}$$

The dielectric loss depends upon the loss tangent, *tan θ*, in the dielectric material, and is given by

$$\alpha_d = \frac{27.3 \sqrt{\epsilon_r} \tan \theta}{\lambda_m} \text{ decibels per meter} \tag{5.74}$$

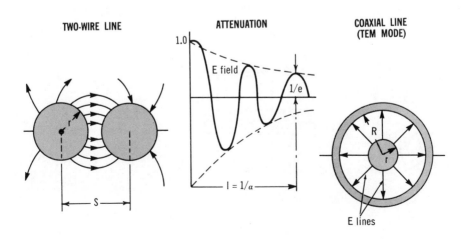

TWO-WIRE LINE   ATTENUATION   COAXIAL LINE (TEM MODE)

116. Coaxial lines — higher order modes

The TEM mode is the principal mode in a coaxial conductor. The TEM mode has the lowest cutoff frequency of all coaxial modes; it propagates right down to direct current. It is possible for higher order modes of both the TE and TM variety to propagate in a coaxial line, and if they can, they will, unless extreme care is taken to suppress them. Generally, coaxial cables are not used at frequencies high enough to permit higher order modes. The reason is not only to avoid the excitation of higher order modes and their attendant loss in power, but also to avoid the penalty of excessively heavy attenuation of the principal mode.

The next lowest order mode, after the TEM, is a TE mode that resembles the $TE_{1,0}$ mode in rectangular waveguide. Its configuration is illustrated. No simple, exact expression exists for expressing the cutoff frequency, f_c, of the TE modes, or of the TM modes either. Their determination depends upon solving a complex transcendental equation.

A rule-of-thumb expression exists for the cutoff wavelength, λ_c, of higher order $TE_{n,0}$ modes. This is given by

$$\lambda_c \cong \frac{2\pi}{n} \left(\frac{R + r}{2} \right) \tag{5.75}$$

For the $TE_{1,0}$ configuration, it is seen that $\lambda_c = 2\pi\overline{R}$, where $\overline{R}$ is the mean radius, so that λ_c equals the mean circumference.

For the TM modes, the E fields must fall to zero at both inner- and outer-conductor interior surfaces. Thus—by analogy wth waveguides—the lowest order TM mode can exist when the spacing $(R - r)$ equals approximately a half wavelength.

All higher order modes, below cutoff, attenuate as illustrated.

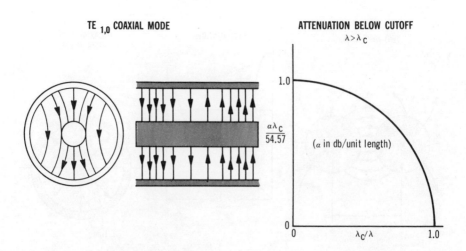

TE $_{1,0}$ COAXIAL MODE

ATTENUATION BELOW CUTOFF
$\lambda > \lambda_c$

1.0

$\dfrac{\alpha\lambda_c}{54.57}$ (α in db/unit length)

0

0   λ_c/λ 1.0

117. Rectangular waveguides — higher order modes

The $TE_{1,0}$ is the principal mode in a rectangular waveguide. Higher order modes of either the $TE_{m,n}$ or the $TM_{m,n}$ types can propagate when the free-space wavelength, λ, is smaller than the cutoff wavelength, λ_c. For both TE and TM waves we have

$$\lambda_c = 2/\sqrt{(m/a)^2 + (n/b)^2} \tag{5.76}$$

where a and b are the internal waveguide dimensions. However, neither m nor n can equal zero for TM waves. Maxwell's equation indicates that *all* fields are then zero for such conditions. Similarly, the TEM mode cannot exist in a rectangular waveguide.

The waveguide wavelength is related to the cutoff wavelength as

$$\lambda/\lambda_g = \sqrt{1 - (\lambda/\lambda_c)^2} \tag{5.77}$$

for TE and TM waves of all orders. Equation 5.77 will be seen as that given in Chapter 2 for the $TE_{1,0}$ mode when $\lambda_c = 2a$. Similarly, the relationships, $V_p V_g = c^2$ and $V_p = f\lambda_g$, also apply universally.

Following the definition of impedance for a TEM wave, the impedance of the rectangular waveguide is defined as the ratio of *transverse* electric field to transverse magnetic field. If μ_1 and ϵ_1 are characteristic of the medium within the rectangular waveguide whose intrinsic impedance $\eta_1 = \sqrt{\mu_1/\epsilon_1}$, then the characteristic impedance for TE modes is

$$Z_0(TE) = \eta_1/\sqrt{1 - (\lambda/\lambda_c)^2} \tag{5.78}$$

and, for TM modes,

$$Z_0(TM) = \eta_1\sqrt{1 - (\lambda/\lambda_c)^2} \tag{5.79}$$

A choice of rectangular waveguide dimensions, $a/b = 2/1$, has been fixed upon as standard. This permits about a 2:1 operation bandwidth for the $TE_{1,0}$ mode while avoiding the propagation of higher order modes.

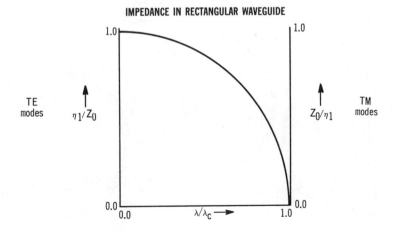

IMPEDANCE IN RECTANGULAR WAVEGUIDE

118. Circular waveguide

The hollow pipe of circular cross section is useful as a transmission line, particularly in the application of a rotary joint. Operating in the $TM_{0,1}$ mode, the circular waveguide has both physical and electrical symmetry about a longitudinal axis. Thus, one of two abutted circular waveguides may be rotated about this axis with respect to the other without altering physical or electrical relationships. In the $TM_{0,1}$ mode, the magnetic field is a set of circles concentric with the guide; in the $TE_{0,1}$ mode, the electric field consists of concentric circles. Neither one of these modes is dominant, however, since the $TE_{1,1}$ mode has the longest cutoff wavelength.

Cutoff wavelength in a circular waveguide depends upon the inside radius, r, of the waveguide and upon the mode type. Cutoff is determined by the relationship

$$\lambda_c = 2\pi r/u_{m,n} \qquad (5.80)$$

where u is a constant that differs from every $TE_{m,n}$ and $TM_{m,n}$ type. For the mode types mentioned above we have:

$$\text{For } TE_{1,1} \qquad u = 1.841$$
$$\text{For } TM_{0,1} \qquad u = 2.405$$
$$\text{For } TE_{0,1} \qquad u = 3.832$$

The $TE_{0,1}$ mode in circular waveguide has extremely low attenuation characteristics when the operating frequency is far enough from cutoff. This property is very valuable for piping electromagnetic energy over long distances. However, this is not done easily because of energy conversion to other modes. Not only do $TE_{1,1}$ and $TM_{0,1}$ modes have longer cutoff wavelength, but $TE_{2,1}$ and $TM_{1,1}$ as well. If used at all in this manner, mode filtering and extremely tight guidance tolerances are required.

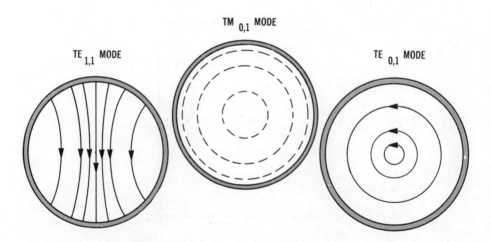

TE$_{1,1}$ MODE   TM$_{0,1}$ MODE   TE$_{0,1}$ MODE

119. Other types — ridge waveguide

The transmission lines previously considered are the "workhorses" of microwave engineering. However, a large variety of other types are employed upon occasion, including the E line, fin line, strip transmission line, and ridged waveguide, to mention but a few. The last two types presently enjoy somewhat greater usage than the others and will be described in greater detail.

The ridge waveguide may be operated, in its dominant $TE_{1,0}$ mode, over a considerably broader range than the rectangular waveguide. The cutoff frequency of the ridged waveguide for the same a dimension may be considerably reduced below that of the rectangular waveguide. At the same time, the cutoff frequency for higher order modes—$TE_{2,0}$ and $TE_{3,0}$—may be increased. Ridge waveguides may have single- or double-ridge cross sections, as shown in the figure.

Ridge waveguides have the disadvantage compared to rectangular waveguides of greater attenuation per unit length and reduced power-handling capacity. The latter deficiency may be partially compensated by pressurization. Because of its form factor, the ridge waveguide lends itself to greater pressurization.

The smaller the ratio, b'/b, the greater the capacitive loading, and the slower the phase velocity of the guide. For a standard guide for which $a/b = 2/1$, the value of $a'/a \cong 0.45$ is optimum if the objective is a maximum reduction in the $TE_{1,0}$ mode cutoff frequency. On the other hand, if the achievement of maximum bandwidth is the objective, an optimum value of $a'/a \cong 0.3$.

SINGLE-RIDGE   DOUBLE-RIDGE

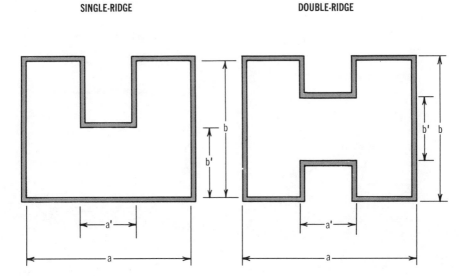

120. Strip transmission line

Strip transmission line is employed at microwave frequencies at low power levels when low cost, small size, or minimal weight is of critical importance. In cross section, balanced strip transmission line consists of a thin metallic conductor or strip centered between two wider metallic plates, or vestigial ground planes. The strip is sometimes supported at intervals along its length by a low-loss plastic, sometimes embedded in a low-loss foam matrix, and sometimes afforded rigidity by metallizing a thin plastic strip.

In contrast to the balanced strip line previously discussed, the slab line is an unbalanced line. As such, it suffers greater radiation losses than the balanced line. By virtue of its construction, slab line is also affected by greater dielectric losses and mode conversion losses (it sustains a surface wave mode). The slab line advantage resides in its ease of construction. One surface of a dielectric slab is metallized to form a continuous ground plane. The other has a thin plating of copper that can be cut or etched to form strip circuitry.

A nearly pure TEM mode exists in the strip transmission line that minimizes radiation losses at bends or corners in the line routing. The width of the ground is restricted to be below cutoff for modes of the $TE_{m,0}$ type. For the slab line, the lack of symmetry and the dielectric-air interface cause distortions in the E field lines. The impedance of slab line is therefore frequency sensitive and susceptible to mode-conversion losses at any discontinuity. The surface-wave mode is one that can exist at a dielectric-conductor interface (it needs no strip). Precautions must therefore be taken to avoid its excitation.

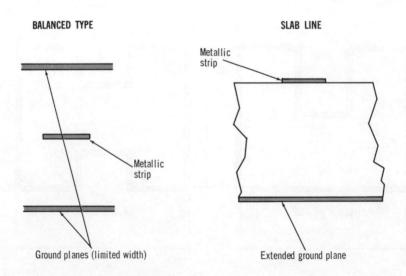

BALANCED TYPE

SLAB LINE

Metallic
strip

Metallic
strip

Ground planes (limited width)

Extended ground plane

Summary of Chapter 5

Waveguides are used as transmission lines at microwave frequencies in order to minimize losses. If the waveguide is limited to single-mode operation, transmission line theory evolved for low-frequency lines may be applied directly. The impedance transformation along a transmission line may be completely described in terms of a sending plus a reflected wave. Although the current and voltage for each wave are cophasal, their sum is usually complex. The input or characteristic impedance of an infinitely long, uniform transmission line is purely resistive. A finite length of line, terminated in its characteristic impedance appears to be infinitely long and is therefore reflectionless. Maximum power may thus be delivered to a transmission line when the load matches the characteristic impedance.

Reactive waveguide loads or obstacles both reflect and store energy in their immediate vicinity. A short-circuited line is purely reactive and is inductive at the load end of the line, whereas an open-circuited line is capacitive. However, at a distance of $\lambda_g/4$ from the load, the capacitive reactive is transformed to inductive, and vice versa. By measurement of the impedance of a lossless transmission line, both open-circuited and short-circuited, its characteristic impedance may be determined. A $\lambda_g/4$ length of line of the proper root-mean-square impedance may be used as a transformer between two lines of dissimilar impedance. A $\lambda_g/2$ length of line of any impedance will transform its output impedance to its input.

Transmission lines dealing with series elements are best handled using impedances, but shunt elements are best handled using admittances. Analogous impedance and admittance transmission line equations exist, and both may be readily solved using the Smith chart.

Questions

1. What is the normalized impedance at the load if $V_s = 10$ volts and $V_r = 1.0$ volts? Plot the phasor relationships of V_s, V_r, I_s, and I_r at the load for $R_o = 60$ ohms.

2. If $V_s = 10 + j3$ volts and $V_r = 1 + j0.6$ volts, what is Z_L? Plot the phasor relationship at the load for $R_0 = 60$ ohms.

3. What are the values of ρ and τ and the power dissipated in the load for question 1? For question 2? Plot the values of ρ and τ at $\lambda/8$, $\lambda/4$, and $\lambda/2$ from the load.

4. For a particular transmission line, it is found that $Z_{sc} = j150$ and $Z_{oc} = -j90$. Find (a) Z_0, and (b) the distance to the load.

5. A load has a normalized admittance of $1 + j0.4$. If the load is matched by a susceptance of magnitude 0.4, where should it be placed with respect to the load? How is the total electrical length of the line changed thereby?

6. A coaxial line has an inner conductor radius of 1/8 in. and an outer of 3/8 in. What is the characteristic impedance? What is the cutoff frequency for the $TE_{1,0}$ mode?

121. Introduction

In the early chapters of this book we considered how electromagnetic energy is transferred from one point to another—both in free space and in bounded media. In later chapters we limited our interest to the microwave portion of the electromagnetic spectrum. We have studied various types of transmission lines, and in a sense, have already considered some microwave components. In this region of the spectrum, the size of the boundary structures is comparable to a wavelength, and the fabrication and assembly tolerances for such structures is small compared with a wavelength. This factor—coupled with the availability of coherent, generating sources of energy—makes possible the design of components utilizing precise phase control. It should therefore not be at all surprising to the reader if, at microwave frequencies, the number of possible components should prove to be enormously greater than at, say, infrared or optical frequencies. Such is, indeed, the case.

A vast assortment of microwave components now exists, and the arsenal of available designs is proliferating at an enormous pace. This chapter will be restricted primarily to a consideration of waveguide components. Even the variety of standard waveguide hardware is too numerous to cover adequately in one short chapter, let alone the new developments involving solid-state and plasma devices. We may make this restriction without sacrifice to our objective, for a textbook on basic microwaves should certainly not attempt to be all-encompassing. Our purpose is to describe a selected number of different components, primarily to illuminate general design principles and only secondarily to indicate the available variety.

It is even difficult to classify microwave components according to a limited number of functions. However, by stretching definitions a little, we can fairly well sort microwave components into the following four categories: (1) coupling devices, (2) attenuating devices, (3) phase-shifting devices, and (4) detecting devices.

No attempt whatever will be made to describe how these components are assembled to perform a system or subsystem function. This falls within the purview of microwave engineering. Nor will any attempt be made to discuss the applications of cryogenics to the achievement of extremely low-loss components or low-noise detectors. Although these may be considered "basic" in a few short years, presently they are at the forefront of the art and, as such, beyond the scope of this book.

Important though it is, the design of practical microwave "plumbing" parts—such as flanges, connectors, cables, windows, bead supports, pressurization considerations, and the like—will also not be considered. Component designs for these may be readily found in catalogues or in handbooks.

Having stated what we will not consider, we turn, then, to waveguide components and first to a consideration of coupling devices.

122. Coupling devices — starting sections

Transitions between two different types of transmission lines involve different mode configurations. The design of transitions must be compatible with the E-line boundary conditions for both lines at their common junction. Conversely, if it is desired to *suppress* an unwanted higher order mode, a configuration is chosen to be incompatible with the boundary conditions required for that mode.

Consider the transition between a coaxial line and a rectangular wave-guide—known as a *starting section*. When the coaxial line abuts on the broad wall of the waveguide, boundary conditions in both transmission lines are suitable when the outer conductor terminates on a circular hole of equal diameter at the broad wall and the center conductor penetrates the b dimension of the guide. If the $TE_{1,0}$ mode is to be excited, the probe is placed centrally with respect to the a dimension. This placement assures compatibility with a cosine distribution by virtue of symmetry and location of the maximum E field. By proper placement of two like transitions, fed 180° apart in phase, the $TE_{2,0}$ mode can be excited.

Although it is possible to extend the center conductor entirely across the b dimension (an inductive probe), more commonly a shallow penetration or capacitive coupling is used. The capacitive probe is usually capped with a conductive hemisphere in order to increase its bandwidth and especially to increase its power-handling capability. The over-all penetration depth is selected for the best impedance match.

Notice that the probe is placed a distance $\lambda_g/4$ from one end of the waveguide, where a short is placed. This short is transformed to the vicinity of the probe entry as an open, or infinite, impedance in parallel with the probe.

COAX-WAVEGUIDE TRANSITIONS

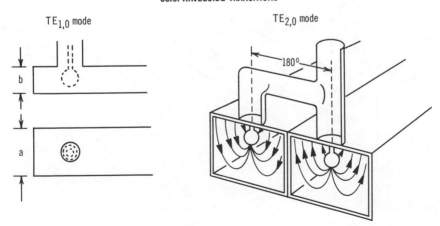

$TE_{1,0}$ mode $TE_{2,0}$ mode

123. Coupling devices — directional coupler

A directional coupler transfers energy from a primary to an adjacent— otherwise independent—secondary transmission line. It is usually required that the coupled power, P_c, travel unidirectionally in the secondary line. This is never fully attainable, and some unwanted energy, P_L, flows in the reverse direction and is dumped into a matched load. Usually, the sum of P_c plus P_L is small compared with the transmitted power, P_T.

The ratio of P_c to the power incident upon the coupler, P_I, is known as the coupling. It is assumed that the coupled power sees a matched load.

$$\text{Coupling}_{(db)} = 10 \log (P_I/P_c) \qquad (6.1)$$

The ratio of P_c to P_L is a measure of the suppression of energy in the unwanted direction and is known as the *directivity*.

$$\text{Directivity}_{(db)} = 10 \log (P_c/P_L) \qquad (6.2)$$

Let us assume that two identical waveguides have one narrow wall in common and that they are coupled by two identical circular holes, whose center-to-center separation is denoted by s.

Since the waveguides and coupling holes are presumed to be identical, energy coupled at hole 2 interferes constructively with that from hole 1 in the forward direction regardless of the separation, s. In the reverse direction, the best directivity is obtained when $s = \lambda_g/4$, for then energy that is coupled at hole 2 and proceeds toward the load travels a distance of $\lambda_g/2$ with respect to energy coupled at hole 1, and destructive interference ensues.

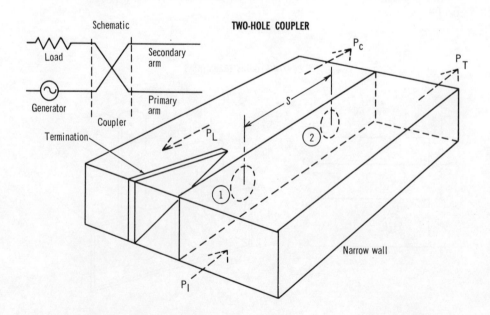

124. Coupling devices—Bethe hole coupler

Either an electric or magnetic dipole field, or their combination, surrounds any small probe, loop, or coupling hole element, whatever its shape, provided only that its dimensions be small enough compared with the wavelength. For example, the field of the short probe starting section just discussed is that of an electric dipole, whereas that of the circular hole in the common narrow waveguide wall represents a magnetic dipole. An electric and a magnetic dipole field are illustrated.

Notice that the coupled electric dipole field is parallel with the exciting E field, but that, near the hole where the coupled E field is strongest, the coupled H field is antiparallel with the exciting H field. Simultaneous excitation of electric and magnetic dipoles thus phased can result in a reverse-direction coupler.

Such an effect is achieved when the coupling hole is located in a common broad wall of two adjacent waveguides. In order to achieve a high directivity, the secondary arm is rotated by an angle, $\theta = \theta_0$. The purpose of the rotation is to reduce the coupled field caused by the magnetic coupling to equality with that caused by the E-field coupling in the direction of the termination.

In the vicinity of the coupling hole the electric dipole field is circularly symmetric and does not vary with θ, whereas the magnetic dipole lines parallel the exciting H field. Of the two, the magnetic dipole usually excites the larger field in the drection of the termination. Thus it is possible to rotate the secondary arm to angle θ_0 without affecting the electric field coupling and thereby to reduce the field caused by the magnetic coupling following a cosine θ function. This type of coupler is named after its inventor, Hans Bethe.

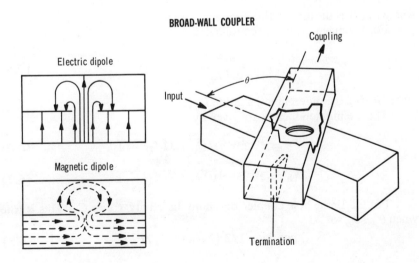

BROAD-WALL COUPLER

Electric dipole

Magnetic dipole

Coupling

Input

θ

Termination

125. Coupling devices — coupling formulas

Coupling formulas may be derived for either common narrow-wall or common broad-wall couplers by assuming infinitely thin coupling walls and then decreasing the value so derived by a factor that will account for a waveguide-below-cutoff attenuation for a thickness t through the small hole. The particular attenuation factor is properly chosen on the basis of (1) the shape of the hole (whether round, rectangular, or otherwise), (2) the coupling type (whether electric or magnetic), and (3) the mode configuration in the hole. The formulas given below pertain only to small circular holes.

1. *Common narrow wall*—The coupling is purely due to a magnetic dipole and is given by

$$C_H = 20 \log_{10}\left(\frac{\pi d^3 \lambda_g}{6a^3 b}\right) - \frac{32t}{d}\left[1 - \left(\frac{1.71d}{\lambda}\right)^2\right] \tag{6.3}$$

in which d is the hole diameter, a and b the guide dimensions, and t the hole thickness. The term on the left yields the coupling caused by a zero-thickness wall, whereas the term on the right accounts for a $TM_{0,1}$ type mode below cutoff attenuation.

2. *Common broad wall*—This type of hole, as we have seen, couples both to the electric and magnetic fields. The total coupled field is the sum of both contributions.

For the electric dipole coupling,

$$C_E = \frac{\pi d^3}{6ab\lambda_g}\left(\frac{\lambda_g}{\lambda}\right)^2 F_E(t) \tag{6.4}$$

where $F_E(t)$ is the attenuation factor.

For the magnetic dipole coupling,

$$C_H = \frac{\pi d^3}{6ab\lambda_g} \cos\theta\, F_H(t) \tag{6.5}$$

where $F_H(t)$ is a different attenuation factor.

The attenuation factors are given by

$$F_E = e^{(-2\pi t/\lambda)\sqrt{(\lambda/1.31d)^2 - 1}} \tag{6.6}$$

and

$$F_H = e^{(-2\pi t/\lambda)\sqrt{(\lambda/1.71d)^2 - 1}} \tag{6.7}$$

For the Bethe hole coupler optimum directivity, $C_E = C_H$. This is true when $\theta = \theta_0$, so

$$\cos\theta_0 = 1/2\,(\lambda_g/\lambda)^2\,(F_E/F_H) \tag{6.8}$$

126. Coupling devices — waveguide tees

Perhaps the simplest coupler of all is the tee, which divides power equally at a right-angle junction of two waveguides. When a plan view of the junction includes the E vector, it is an E-plane tee; correspondingly, when it includes the H vector, it is an H-plane tee. These tees are shown in perspective and in plan in the figure. Arm A is a branch arm, whereas arms B and C are collinear.

When power is fed into the branch arm of either tee and the collinear arms terminate in matched loads, the power division is equal in the two collinear arms. However, the branch arm sees a small mismatch; some energy is reflected at the junction.

One important difference exists in the performance of the two tees. When the E-plane tee is fed from the branch arm, a phase difference of 180° exists between the E fields traveling down the collinear arms. For the H-plane tee, the E fields in the collinear arms are cophasal. The E-plane tee is known as a *series* tee and the H-plane as a *shunt* tee. The reason for this terminology is apparent if one considers current flow. For the E-plane tee, longitudinal currents flowing in the collinear arms are interrupted in series by the branch arm, whereas for the H-plane tee, transverse currents are interrupted in shunt by the branch arm.

By reciprocity, it follows that if both collinear arms of an H-plane tee are fed equal, cophasal power, all the energy will travel down the branch arm. Similarly, if both collinear arms of an E-plane tee are fed equal, anti-phased power, all the power will also appear there.

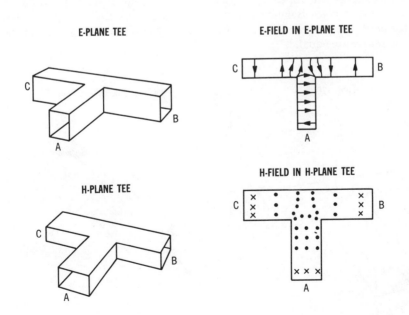

E-PLANE TEE

E-FIELD IN E-PLANE TEE

H-PLANE TEE

H-FIELD IN H-PLANE TEE

127. Coupling devices — the magic tee

The magic tee is a four-port, common junction of a series tee and a shunt tee. When the receiving arms are all terminated in matched loads, this tee has the following properties:

1. When energy is fed to the series arm, it divides equally between both collinear arms, and none appears at the shunt arm termination.
2. When energy is fed to the shunt arm, it divides equally between both collinear arms, and none appears at the series arm termination.
3. Phase relationships for the first two cases are precisely the same as when inputs are fed to simple series tees or simple shunt tees.
4. When energy is fed to either one of the collinear arms, energy appears at all three of the remaining arms.

Magic tees, besides their use as 3-db dividers, find applications in balanced or bridge circuits. Balanced mixer and phase bridge circuits are two such applications.

For the balanced mixer usage, a matched detector is placed in each of the two collinear arms. Local oscillator power fed into the shunt arm is then completely decoupled from the signal power simultaneously fed into the series arm.

For the phase bridge application, an object is to avoid the errors that reflections might cause on the measured phase of the test piece. If the input signal is fed to the shunt arm, reflections from the test piece can be matched out by the introduction of an equal reflection at the input to the phase shifter. If the line lengths to the reflections differ by $\lambda_g/4$, all the reflected energy will appear at the load near the input; none will recirculate around the bridge. Balance of the bridge is indicated by a null at the detector on the output series arm when the phase of the test piece and the phase shifter are equal.

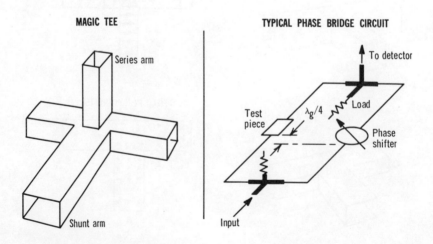

MAGIC TEE — Series arm, Shunt arm

TYPICAL PHASE BRIDGE CIRCUIT — To detector, Test piece, $\lambda_g/4$, Load, Phase shifter, Input

128. Coupling devices — hybrid junctions

The magic tee is but one example of a class of couplers having similar properties. Such couplers are known as hybrid junctions after the low-frequency, hybrid-coil prototype that exhibits the same properties. Other forms of hybrid junctions are the folded tee, the "rat race," and the cobrid, or coaxial hybrid tee. All have very similar performance capabilities; a choice between them is based upon other considerations, such as consistency of transmission line types or ease of packaging.

The rat race is formed from a waveguide ring structure with a mean circumference of $3\lambda_g/2$. Four arms, spaced $\lambda_g/4$ apart, connect with the ring. If the ring is folded in the E plane, series connections are made to the ring, and if folded in the H plane, shunt connections. The operation of the ring is the same in both cases.

If energy is fed to arm A, it divides equally at the junction with the ring, half of it passing clockwise and the other half counter-clockwise. In arms B and D, these two components rejoin cophasally but are in antiphase at arm C. Consequently, all the energy divides equally between arms B and D, and arm C is isolated. Similarly, if energy is fed to arm C, it divides equally between B and D, and arm A is isolated.

As noted previously, care must be observed to match impedances; otherwise the properties of the hybrid junction will not be retained. For the series rat race of Z_0 arm impedance, the impedance of the ring should equal $Z_0/\sqrt{2}$. For the shunt connected cobrid shown, the ring impedance should equal $Z_0\sqrt{2}$.

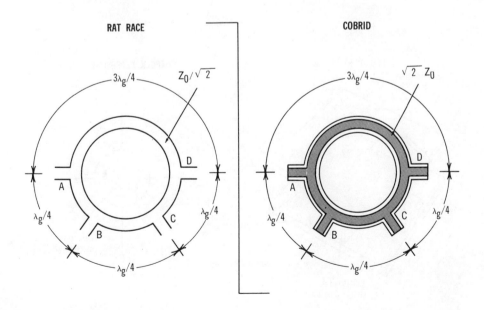

Microwave Components

129. Coupling devices — circulator

The circulator is a common, multijunction device comprising three or more ports; it possesses the property of coupling energy between adjacent ports in only one direction around the device and isolating non-adjacent ports. For example, energy entering port 1 of the device couples entirely to port 2, with essentially no energy appearing at the other ports; energy entering port 2 couples entirely to port 3; and, for a three-port device, energy entering port 3 couples entirely to port 1. Thus, energy circulates around the junction in one direction only.

The reader may well protest that this property violates reciprocity, and indeed it does. To achieve this nonreciprocal behavior, a nonlinear ferrite material is located at the junction. The circulator is but one of a family of interesting devices—including isolators, duplexers, phase rotators, and modulators—that rely for their operation upon the nonreciprocal properties of ferrites.

Ferrite materials are composed of mixtures of iron oxides with other oxides of bivalent metals, such as nickel or cobalt. The constituents are ground, mixed, and fired at high temperatures to produce a material with a large net permeability, like soft iron ferromagnets, but also with a low electrical conductivity, like ceramics. Electrons of a ferrite in a waveguide immersed in a d-c magnetic field behave similarly to a precessing gyroscope. Depending upon the sense of the r-f phase, r-f energy will either reinforce the precession or oppose it. Thus r-f energy traveling in one direction will couple differently to the medium than energy traveling in the opposite direction. This is the basis for the nonreciprocal behavior of the circulator.

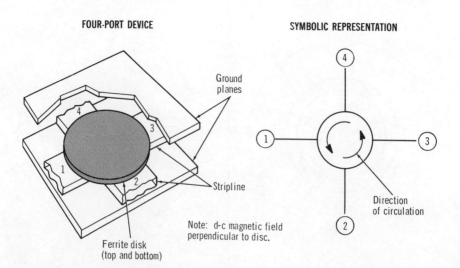

FOUR-PORT DEVICE   SYMBOLIC REPRESENTATION

Ground planes

Stripline

Ferrite disk (top and bottom)

Note: d-c magnetic field perpendicular to disc.

Direction of circulation

130. Coupling devices — rotary joint

A stationary waveguide connects to a rotating waveguide by means of a rotary joint. Obviously, the axis of the rotary joint must lie on the axis of rotation. To accommodate the geometrical limitations, a waveguide mode in the rotary joint must have axial symmetry. For this reason, rotary joints popularly employ the coaxial mode or the $TM_{0,1}$ mode in circular waveguides. Another configuration, almost perfectly symmetrical, is the binary rotary joint. From a single input, connection is made by binary branching to multiple-coupling probes disposed uniformly about a circle, inside which a cylindrical conductor rotates. The output coupling, displaced along the cylinder, is identical to the input.

In order to effect continuity across the gap in the circular waveguide, a quarterwave "choke" section is added. The annual space between the choke and rotor forms a coaxial waveguide. Its object is to reflect a short across the gap by means of a transformed open, one-quarter wavelength distant. However, the physical coaxial "open," because of edge effects, is not a perfect open. Therefore, a second backup choke is added to increase the impedance at the "open." The backup choke is shorted at one end and reflects a high impedance one-quarter wavelength away.

A circular matching obstacle, aligned with the rectangular waveguide axis but eccentrically displaced with respect to the circular waveguide, is used to match from the $TE_{1,0}$ to the $TM_{0,1}$ mode. To ensure that no residue $TE_{1,1}$ mode propagates in the circular waveguide, a metallic ring tending to short this mode is located symmetrically with respect to the circular waveguide portion.

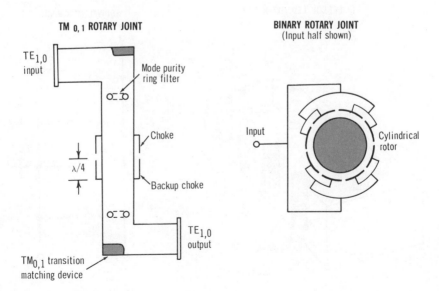

131. Coupling devices — microwave filter

The simple straight section of rectangular waveguide passes all frequencies above its dominant mode cut-off frequency and reflects all frequencies below. Behaving thus, it displays all the characteristics of a high-pass microwave filter. Still other filters can be constructed with low-pass, band-pass, band-rejection, or harmonic-rejection functions. Filters generally are iterative cavity structures or obstacles, deriving their filtering properties by virtue of a rapid phase change with frequency. One of the simpler types, which exemplifies filter action, is the direct-coupled, band-pass filter shown in the figure.

Quarter-wave cavity sections are isolated along the length of the waveguide by the paired emplacement of inductive irises. Each cavity may be separately tuned near resonance by a tuning screw centrally placed on the broad waveguide wall. The net equivalent circuit is a set of inductive susceptances spaced at intervals along a transmission line.

When the frequency of operation lies within the passband, energy reflected by the iris discontinuities cancels out. However, when the frequency lies outside the passband, a high VSWR is set up. The steepness of the rise in the attenuation characteristics at the edge of the passband (the filter skirts) is directly related to the number of filter sections employed. This desirable characteristic is accompanied by an unwanted rise in the attenuation of the filter in the passband.

An alternative to the direct-coupled filter is the shunt-coupled filter, which handles higher power levels.

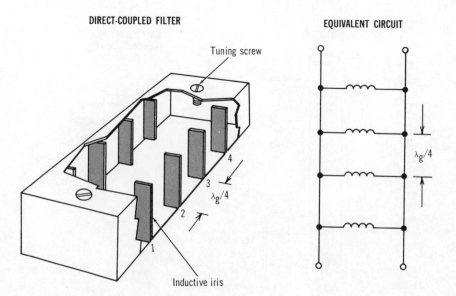

132. Coupling devices — resonant windows and posts

The equivalent circuit of a capacitive iris and an inductive iris—both located simultaneously at the same point in a transmission line, thus forming a rectangular opening—is a parallel resonant circuit in shunt with the transmission line. At resonance, the circuit-shunt impedance is much higher than the characteristic impedance of the line and the net impedance upset is small. The resonant iris thus forms a highly transmissive window. When a low-loss plastic is sealed across the rectangular opening, a pressure window is formed that is suitable for the containment of appreciable pressure differential across its face.

R. Muchmore has found a simple method of predicting the resonant dimensions of a resonant iris. Resonance occurs when the corners of the rectangular opening fall on symmetrical hyperbolas, as sketched in the figure. A small compensation in these dimensions must be made when the window contains pressure in order to offset the increased capacitance of the plastic seal.

Though not so obviously a coupling device as a pressure window, the tuned post is so similar in behavior that its discussion logically follows here. A single, narrow metallic post across the entire *b* dimension of parallel plates presents an inductance in shunt with the waveguide. A pair of metallic hollow cylinders surrounding the post present a capacitance in shunt with the waveguide. Together, they form a parallel-resonant circuit in shunt with the waveguide. To increase the capacitance of the metallic cylinders, it is sometimes necessary to embed the post in a low-loss dielectric material, as shown.

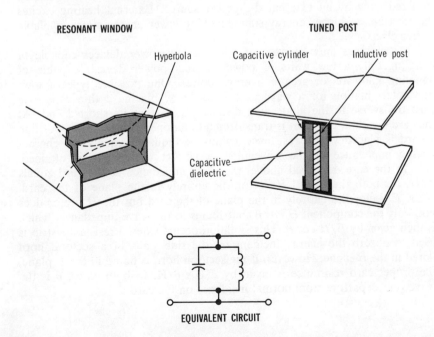

RESONANT WINDOW   TUNED POST

Hyperbola   Capacitive cylinder   Inductive post

Capacitive dielectric

EQUIVALENT CIRCUIT

133. Attenuating devices — attenuation

Attenuating devices find many uses at microwave frequencies. Attenuators are used in order to (1) isolate a source from reflections from its load so as to preclude frequency pulling; (2) adjust the signal level, as in one arm of a microwave bridge circuit; (3) measure signal levels, as with a calibrated attenuator; (4) measure delivered power when employed as a calorimeter; and (5) absorb total power (act as a perfect termination), as in a radar silence application.

Diverse materials are suitable for attenuating microwave energy. However, all have certain properties in common, for example: (1) the skin depth in the material is of the order of magnitude or greater than the wavelength, and (2) the molecular structure or state admits of a loss mechanism. These properties are in contrast on the one hand with metals, whose profuse supply of free surface electrons bars penetration of the electromagnetic energy, and on the other hand with lossless dielectrics, whose electrons are bound by the crystalline structure.

When an electromagnetic wave penetrates a low-loss medium, free electrons are excited to oscillation about their average positions, reactive energy is stored, and the velocity of propagation in the medium is reduced. In a lossy medium, the free electrons accelerated by the electromagnetic wave are either captured by or transmit part of their energy to the molecular structure; this energy is supplied by the electromagnetic field.

Materials such as carbon that have unsaturated outer electronic shells capable of acting both as a donors and acceptors of electrons make effective lossy materials. A heated, filamentary wire, or bolometer, acts similarly. To act as an efficient detector of microwave radiation, the wire is heated to a red glow by an external d-c power source. External heating excites the electrons to higher energy states, making lower energy states available to free electrons.

Attenuators may be fixed or variable low-power devices capable of handling only a few watts of power or high-power devices capable of handling kilowatts or greater average power. One possible type of low-power termination for a waveguide is made by placing a thin resistance card transverse to the guide at a distance $\lambda_g/4$ from its shorted end. At the card position, the short is transformed to an open. When at this position a card is placed whose resistance (ohms per square) equals the characteristic impedance of the waveguide, a perfect termination is attained.

In the case described above, the wave impedance at the card equals E/H, for both the E and H vectors lie entirely in the plane of the card. If the E vector lies entirely in the plane of the card but the H vector does not, only the component $H \cos \theta$ contributes to the wave impedance, which is then given by $E/H \cos \theta$. This situation occurs when a resistance strip is used to absorb the energy incident on the side walls of a sectoral horn flared in the H plane. However, if the sectoral horn is flared in the E plane, the proper card resistance is given by $E \cos \theta/H$. In both cases, θ is the wavefront departure from normal incidence on the card.

134. Attenuating devices — low-power attenuators

Low-power attenuators usually employ a thin film of carbon sprayed over a thin bakelite or glass support card. The leading edge is tapered for a depth of at least $\lambda_g/2$ so as to minimize reflected energy. The card is placed in the waveguide with its edge parallel both to its center line and the E field. In this orientation the E field can most effectively accelerate the free electrons.

For maximum attenuation, fixed-card attenuators are placed midway between the two narrow walls. Variable attenuator cards are of two types —flap attenuators and side-wall attenuators.

FLAP ATTENUATOR   SIDE-WALL ATTENUATOR

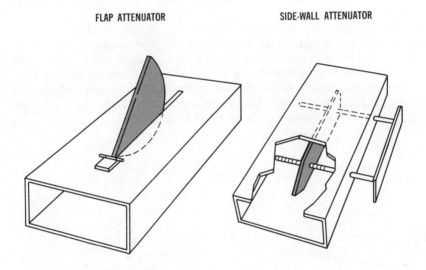

Flap attenuators are introduced through a nonradiating, longitudinal slot centered on one of the broadwall faces. This is easy to construct and serves adequately for laboratory use. However, when the card is partially inserted, the waveguide field penetrates it and radiates externally to the waveguide. To overcome this deficiency, and also to preserve the pressure-tight integrity of the waveguide, the side-wall attenuator is used. In this type of attenuator, two cylindrical rods penetrate both narrow walls of the waveguide and carry the attenuator card at any position from alongside one sidewall, for minimum attenuation, to midway between the sidewalls, for maximum attenuation.

As stated, it is possible to make a perfect termination with a card— whose resistance per square equals the characteristic impedance of the guide —by placing it transverse to the waveguide at a distance of $\lambda_g/4$ from a short. However, use of this attenuator is limited, for it is much more critical and less broad band than longitudinally placed attenuators.

135. Attenuating devices — high power loads

For attenuators, "high power" connotes high *average* power as well as high *peak* power. Peak power may introduce a breakdown problem. High average power is concerned with the heat dissipation problem.

High power loads may be of the type whose material can sustain high temperatures without deterioration. To increase its thermal capacity, the entire waveguide interior is filled with a ceramic, which may include a mixture of carboniferous material. The input edge may be wedge-shaped or stepped for a good match. Heat dissipation includes thermal radiation as a significant mechanism. Further to enhance load power capabilities, the guide may have metallic fins mounted on it, to transfer heat by convection to the environment, or coils carrying liquid coolant wrapped around it, to assist conduction.

Water loads (see photograph) are to be distinguished from water-cooled loads. In the former, the water enters the guide medium and directly serves as the lossy medium. The water in the guide is isolated from the rest of the guide in a volume shaped for a good impedance match by a thin, low-loss, plastic wedge. Water circulates through this volume and absorbs and removes the heat. Water has a very high dielectric constant and loss tangent. The water load is ideally suited as a calorimeter.

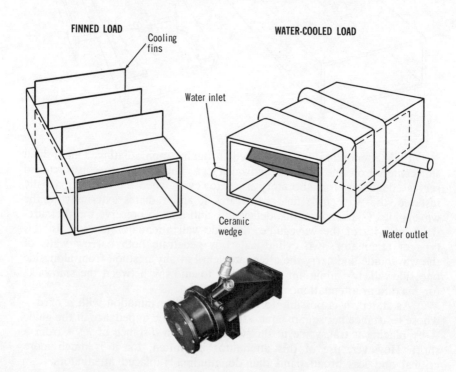

FINNED LOAD

Cooling fins

WATER-COOLED LOAD

Water inlet

Ceramic wedge

Water outlet

136. Attenuating devices — below cutoff attenuators

In a lossless waveguide carrying a propagating mode, the transverse components of both electric and magnetic fields oscillate in time phase. The Poynting vector, S, then points in the direction of propagation. As the longitudinal field components of propagating modes are in time quadrature, the net energy loss into the sidewalls is zero.

When a lossless waveguide is excited by energy below cutoff, the steady state transverse components are in time quadrature. The net vector, S, in the direction of propagation is therefore zero. Along the length of the waveguide, the fields fall off exponentially from their values at the exciting source. Reactive energy is alternately stored in the waveguide and returned to the source each cycle.

If a probe is inserted in a waveguide excited below cutoff, at some distance from the exciting source, it is possible to alter the quadrature relationship of the fields slightly and to abstract energy. In fact, the value of $E \times H$ in the direction of propagation automatically adjusts itself to the degree of coupling of the probe. Thus, the phase of the coupled energy varies with the coupled power. It is also possible to transmit energy through a below cutoff waveguide which is connected between two propagating transmission lines. The coupled energy will depend upon the attenuation of the below cutoff attenuator and is given by

$$\alpha = \frac{54.57}{\lambda_c} \left(\frac{\sqrt{\lambda^2 - \lambda_c^2}}{\lambda} \right) \text{db/unit length} \tag{6.9}$$

From Eq. 6.9 one sees that if the frequency is far from cutoff ($\lambda \gg \lambda_c$), the factor in parentheses approaches unity, and α approaches

$$\alpha \cong 54.57/\lambda_c \text{ db/unit length} \tag{6.10}$$

When λ exceeds $10\lambda_c$, the error in Eq. 6.10 is less than 0.5ϵ per cent, where ϵ is the dielectric constant entirely filling the waveguide medium.

Equations 6.9 and 6.10 apply equally to all possible cutoff modes. Notice that when the conditions for Eq. 6.10 are met, the attenuation is linearly proportional to the length of the below cutoff section of the waveguide and is independent of frequency. These conditions serve admirably as the basis for an attenuation standard. In constructing such a standard, care must be taken at the input and output to avoid the excitation of high-order modes—which may follow the law of Eq. 6-9 even though the dominant mode is sufficiently removed from cutoff.

A convenient way to construct a waveguide standard attenuator, then, is to cut a centered longitudinal slot in a below cutoff waveguide and insert a probe. The absolute value of the coupling, or insertion loss of the attenuator, may not be known accurately, but the attenuation difference at any two probe positions is given by Eq. 6.10. A precision carriage must be constructed to transport the probe, from which all backlash is removed. A relatively broad slot must also be used to minimize variations in the slot-to-probe spacing as the probe travels along the guide.

137. Attenuating devices — switches

On-off microwave switches are the most drastic kinds of attenuating devices. Switches are based either upon change in reflection or transmission properties and may be operated either electrically or mechanically. A solenoid-actuated shutter or shorting plunger is a simple mechanical switch. A gas tube, whose conductive state is changed by a d-c electrical pulse, is a not-so-simple example of an all-electrical device.

Electrically operated microwave switches are used rather than mechanical switches when switching time is important. Low-power (milliwatt-range) diode switches are capable of switching times in the order of tens of nanoseconds. Intermediate-power switches (watt-range), such as ferrite devices, are capable of microsecond switching times.

Mechanically operated switches, on the other hand, enjoy the advantage of greater power-handling capacity, and, sometimes, of less drive-power drain.

Two 3-db hybrids connected in series, with a two-position 0–180° phase shifter in one leg, constitute a useful switch (see figure). Energy at the input divides equally at the first hybrid. Passage through this hybrid delays the signal by 90° in phase. At the second hybrid, all the energy combines in phase at arm 1 and cancels at arm 2. When 180° of phase is inserted at the phase shifter, all the energy combines in arm 2 and cancels in arm 1. By removing the second hybrid and terminating both arms in shorts, a reflection type switch can be made whose principle of operation follows that of the dual hybrid transmission switch.

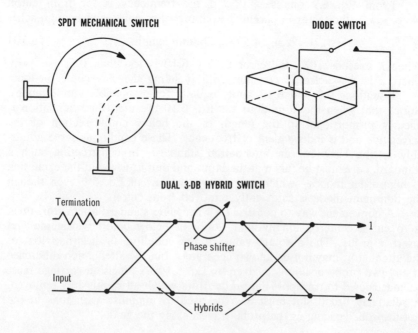

138. Attenuating devices — ferrite modulators

A linearly polarized electromagnetic wave, on passing through a ferrite medium biased to the proper d-c magnetic field strength, will have its plane of polarization rotated. This phenomenon is known as *Faraday rotation*. The same property is also observed when electromagnetic waves of the proper low frequency impinge upon the ionosphere (which is immersed in the earth's magnetic field).

Every linearly polarized wave can be analyzed into two counter-rotating, circularly polarized waves of the same frequency. In a gyrotropic medium—such as a biased ferrite or the ionosphere—one of the two circularly polarized components will strongly couple to the gyro precession of the free electrons. As a result, its propagation velocity will be substantially reduced. The other component will not couple, and its propagation velocity will be relatively unaffected. Upon emergence from the gyrotropic medium, the components recombine to form a linear wave whose plane of polarization depends upon their phase differential.

A simple, low-power ferrite modulator can be built utilizing Faraday rotation. A round ferrite rod, tapered at both ends, is mounted axially in a rectangular waveguide. A solenoid encloses the waveguide. When energized, its d-c magnetic field establishes near-gyromagnetic resonance for the input electromagnetic wave. Varying the coil current varies the output plane of polarization. In the waveguide region excluding the ferrite, only the $TE_{1,0}$ mode can propagate, so the E-field component cross-polarized to the waveguide will be reflected at the ferrite output and will be absorbed at the load.

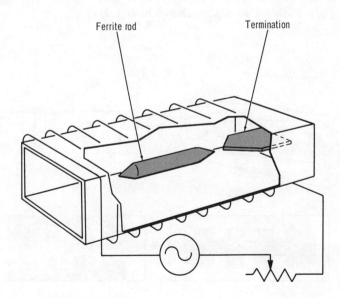

Ferrite rod   Termination

139. Phase shift devices — fixed phase shifters

When absolute phase is important to the operation of an r-f circuit, the simplest alternative usually is to adjust the physical length of the transmission line. When it is required to vary phase without change of system physical layout, phase shifters are used.

All phase shifters function by virtue of the storage of reactive energy in their immediate vicinity. Storage occurs at any discontinuity caused by a change in waveguide cross section, at an obstacle, or throughout a dielectric medium, real or artificial. In such media, electrons are alternately displaced from their equilibrium positions by the r-f field and are then restored by Coulomb forces, returning their energy to the r-f field. The net effect is a reduction in the r-f wavelength, that is, an increase in the phase constant.

In Chapter 4 we referred to a dual-loaded lens having planar-planar surfaces. This lens relies entirely upon fixed-phase shifting elements placed within the individual waveguide cells to alter phase for the lens action. Lengths are varied to adjust phase. The lens elements utilized are comblike metallic strips, shown in Fig. A, supported along the center of the broad wall.

The lens elements concentrate the E lines in their vicinity so that the transverse field distribution departs from cosinusoidal. With the energy concentrated, the comb digit discontinuities produce a large phase delay, thus reducing the waveguide cut-off frequency. Dual-lens action is given by an independent set of loading structures, orthogonal to the first.

If a flat, thin metal plate were inserted into the waveguide of Fig. A, perpendicular to the E field and bifurcating the guide, the field would not be disturbed. The two waveguide halves thus isolated may be rejoined, thus forming the equivalent structures shown in Fig. B.

A) Loaded lens

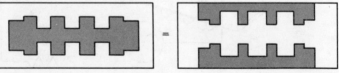

B) Equivalent structures

140. Phase shift devices — variable phase shifters

A waveguide squeeze section can be formed by altering the *a* dimension of the waveguide. A nonradiating longitudinal slot is cut along the waveguide centerline. Then an adjustable C-clamp is attached across the *a* dimension, changing it by differences in applied pressure. Alternatively, one of the narrow walls, physically detached from the rest of the waveguide but electrically "choked" to prevent radiation loss, can be moved in and out to alter the *a* dimension. Many wavelengths of phase change can be achieved in this fashion. During World War II, the airborne Eagle scanner was based upon this principle.

One of the more satisfactory phase shifters, which is limited to a maximum of about 360° of phase shift, is the side-wall phase shifter. Built like the side-wall attenuator, this phase shifter carries a low-loss plastic strip on its carriage in place of the resistance card. It is necessary to taper the output as well as the input of the plastic strip in order to avoid spurious phase effects caused by reflections. Similarly, the electrical width and length of the strip must be chosen so as to avoid high VSWR's caused by internal resonances.

A useful phase shifter is the 3-db hybrid with reflecting shorts whose *relative* phase is locked so that all the power entering arm 1 appears in arm 2. Thus locked together, the ganged arms are slid in unison so that the absolute phase of the output is varied. Since the signal is reflected, the output phase, $2\beta 1$, varies at twice the rate of the waveguide phase constant.

Still another variant consists of the replacement of the sliding shorts with diode shorts. If a number of diodes are spaced along the line and fired together in pairs, a set of quantized phase shifts, rapidly selectable, are afforded.

SIDE WALL   **GANGED SHORTS**

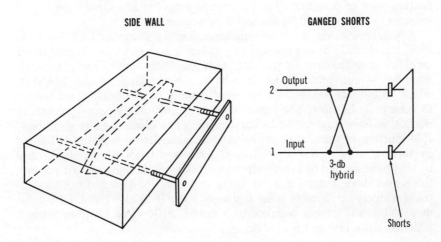

141. Detecting devices — introduction

Detection and absolute measurement of r-f power relies first upon the conversion of r-f power into heat and then the measurement of the rate of production of heat. The technique is directly applicable at high and intermediate power levels, particularly when the r-f source output is relatively constant. At low power levels, or when the output levels vary rapidly, calorimetric techniques must be replaced by less direct methods. For detection methods employed at low power levels, matching is difficult, and the abstraction of all or a known fraction of the incident power becomes correspondingly more difficult.

Fortunately, the measurement merely of relative power is often sufficient, particularly at low power levels. At microwave frequencies low-power sensors are either bolometers or crystal diodes. Bolometers are capable of sustaining higher power levels before burnout than crystals are and utilize relatively inexpensive equipment. On the other hand, crystals may be three or more orders of magnitude more sensitive as detectors than bolometers are, although relatively expensive associated electronic equipment is required to realize this greater sensitivity.

Upon absorbing r-f power, bolometer elements change their resistance. This change is measurable in an a-c or d-c bridge circuit.

Conventional whisker-type crystals rectify the incident r-f fields and provide an output current proportional to the incident r-f power. For greater sensitivity this is accomplished in two stages. At the first detector, an auxiliary frequency, the local oscillator, is mixed with the desired signal. The difference, or intermediate frequency, is then amplified before it is applied to the second, or video detector.

At microwave frequencies, first-stage conversion losses up to 10 db or even greater are typical for whisker-type diodes. Thus detection sensitivity is limited. The recent introduction of varactor diodes has made it possible to avoid this limitation by providing means for low noise amplification prior to detection. The parametric amplifier is a circuit employing varactor diodes and will be discussed subsequently.

A tunnel diode quantum mechanical effect discovered by Esaki in 1957 has recently been exploited to produce a very low noise tunnel diode amplifier at microwave frequencies. This amplifier—unlike the parametric amplifier, whose performance is enhanced by cooling, or the MASER, which requires cooling—does not need cooling to cryogenic temperatures to achieve its benefits. The tunnel diode operates on a negative resistance portion in its voltage-current characteristic. The diode used is a "doped" P-N junction of germanium or gallium-arsenide. Its noise figure is limited by thermal noise across the effective series resistance of the diode, and by shot noise caused by erratic electron crossing of the junction. At present, the tunnel diode amplifier noise figure at S-band is 4 to 5 db. This contrasts with crystal detector noise figures of 8 to 10 db at S-Band. Of course, these values still cannot compete with the MASER noise figure at S-band, which is just a few tenths of a db.

142. Detecting devices — bolometers

The bolometers most used at microwave frequencies are the barreter and the thermistor. The barreter consists of a very fine platinum wire, less than 0.0001 in. in diameter, that is heated to incandescence by an external d-c power source. Incident r-f power causes an increase in the wire resistance. A thermistor consists of a small glass bead containing a semi-conductor composed of a fired mixture of metallic oxides. Contact with the bead is made by two collinear leads that are embedded in it. Incident r-f power causes a decrease in thermistor resistance.

The barreter can detect signals as small as 1 microwatt in power and will handle power nearly as large as 1 watt without burnout. Over any limited portion of this range, its characteristic may be made to match that of a perfect square-law (power) detector. The thermistor characteristic departs appreciably from square-law detection, but the thermistor has the advantage that it can handle several watts of power without burnout.

The barreter cartridge is mounted so that the wire is parallel to the *E* field. It may be located a fixed distance from a waveguide short and be fixed-matched by an iris. Alternatively, the barreter may be mounted in front of a variable short, whose distance is adjusted at each frequency to achieve a good match.

The thermistor couples only loosely to the incident power when aligned parallel to the *E* vector. Tighter coupling can be achieved by bending one of its leads into a loop and orienting the loop to couple to the magnetic component of the r-f field.

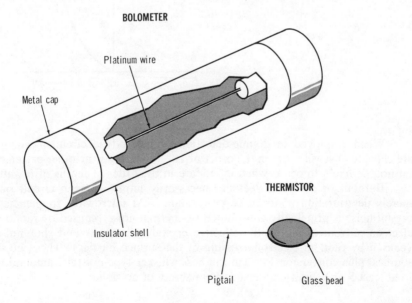

BOLOMETER

Platinum wire

Metal cap

Insulator shell

THERMISTOR

Pigtail

Glass bead

143. Detecting devices — crystals

Semiconductor crystals—particularly silicon, but also germanium—are useful as detectors at microwave frequencies. The crystal is ground into the form of a small cylinder. One end of the cylinder is brought into contact over its entire face with a metallic connector; the other makes contact with the finely sharpened point of a tungsten wire whisker. At the surface of the two dissimilar materials, a work function potential difference exists of a polarity that will assist electron flow from the whisker to the silicon but oppose opposite flow. Rectification of an r-f signal is thereby rendered possible.

The metal-semiconductor potential difference that exists at the opposite end of the crystal tends to oppose the rectification. However, its large contact area and large capacitance (which is in shunt with the contact resistance and therefore bypasses the r-f signal) negates the opposition.

CRYSTAL CARTRIDGE   TYPICAL CRYSTAL CHARACTERISTIC

Tungsten whisker

Silicon crystal

When employed in double-detection or heterodyne circuits, crystals are capable of sensitivities in the order of 10^{-13} watts. At the other extreme, burnout is likely to occur when inputs are in the order of tenths of a watt.

Burnout of a crystal does not necessarily imply an open circuit but merely deterioration of its noise performance. At microwave frequencies, crystal noise is principally contributed by thermal noise (caused by random electron movement across the effective crystal resistance) and shot noise (caused by random electron crossing of the surface barrier). These noise sources, plus conversion loss (in the best whisker-type crystals, amounting to at least 5 db), limit the detection capability of crystals.

144. Detecting devices — varactor diodes

An n-type semiconductor has an excess of electrons, whereas a p-type has a shortage. A varactor diode is a p-n junction of semiconductors (such as gallium arsenide) whose interface capacitance depends upon the voltage applied across the surface—hence the term, *varactor,* standing for variable reactance. By means of this variable capacitance, energy from a "pump" source is transferred to the signal, which is thus amplified. The amplifier based upon this principle is known as a parametric amplifier.

Signal energy gets stored in the capacitance at the varactor diode interface. The stored energy is directly proportional to the capacitance since the energy of an capacitor equals $CV^2/2$. The pump signal is introduced across the diode interface simultaneously with the input signal. It is made much larger than the input signal, and hence its voltage chiefly modulates the capacitance of the junction, thereby affecting the stored energy. When the pump signal is supplied in the right frequency or phase relationship, it is possible to transfer pump energy to the input signal and to amplify it. The methods for accomplishing this are (1) the degenerate, and (2) the nondegenerate, or regenerative.

In the so-called degenerate mode, the pump frequency is exactly double the signal frequency ($f_p = 2f_s$), and their phase relationship is critical. The nondegenerate amplifier introduces an idler circuit resonant at the difference frequency between pump and signal, so that $f_i = f_p - f_s$, and phase relationships are self-adjusting. A circulator is required to isolate the output signal and its load from the input.

The figure of merit for the parametric amplifier is its gain-bandwidth product. Values considerably in excess of 100 megacycles per second are achievable. Internally generated noise can be reduced appreciably by cooling the varactor down to cryogenic temperatures.

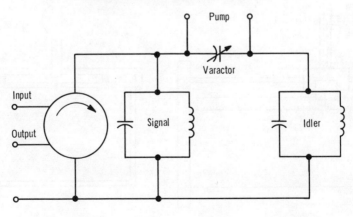

NONDEGENERATE PARAMP EQUIVALENT CIRCUIT

145. Detecting devices — standing wave detector

Possibly the most used and most useful microwave laboratory component is the standing-wave detector. Electrically, the standing wave detector is quite simple, but mechanical precision is required for accurate results.

A nonradiating slot is cut longitudinally for a distance of about $2\lambda_g$ along a transmission line, permitting entry of a probe. The probe position along the transmission line is capable of accurate adjustment and measurement. Probe penetration into the transmission line can be varied, and the probe impedance can be matched at different penetrations by means of a tunable cavity.

Ways are provided to guide the probe carriage accurately, so that neither probe depth nor centering is displaced as it is moved longitudinally. The drive mechanism is selected to eliminate backlash, which otherwise could cause annoyance when one attempts to locate a voltage minimum (even though the readings are unaffected).

In practice, the probe penetration is adjusted to the minimum value consistent with sufficient output signal in order to minimize disturbance of the existing fields in the transmission line.

It is possible, using the standing wave detector; to measure not only the magnitude of VSWR caused by a load but also its phase angle. If the load is shorted, the shift in position of the null will permit the phase angle to be determined. If only the magnitude of VSWR needs to be known as a function of frequency, it is easier to measure the magnitudes of incident and reflected waves with two-directional couplers having high directivities.

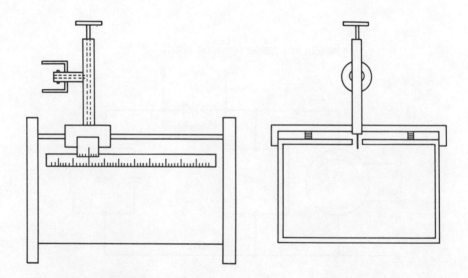

Summary of Chapter 6

Both optical and low-frequency techniques are at the disposal of the present-day designer of microwave components. Precise control of relative phase at different positions inside the components—permitted both by machining tolerances which are small compared with the wavelength at microwave frequencies and by the availability of coherent power sources —makes possible a large variety of devices that are not available at other frequencies.

Couplers are devices which serve as transitions between two transmission lines; they must be designed to match boundary conditions at both. Directivity is a measure of the isolation or efficiency of a coupler. Either electric or magnetic coupling, or a combination of both (the Bethe hole coupler), may be employed, utilizing apertures in either the narrow or the broad wall of a waveguide.

Simple, but extremely useful, couplers are the E-plane and the H-plane tees. The magic tee—along with its variants, the rat-race and the cobrid—is a four-port hybrid junction that offers especially valuable isolation properties.

Ferrites in nonreciprocal configurations may be introduced into couplers in order to fashion circulators and isolators. Reactive structures— both resonant and nonresonant types—may be assembled in order to achieve low-pass, high-pass, and band-pass filters. Resonant reactive structures may also be employed as reflectionless mechanical posts and supports inside microwave transmission lines.

Fixed and variable attenuators are used to isolate power sources, adjust constant signal levels or variable levels (modulators), or measure or absorb delivered power. Attenuators are characterized by large skin depths and also by an atomic structure that permits an electron energy loss mechanism.

Resistance cards that have been coated with carboniferous materials serve as low-loss attenuators. At higher powers, a ceramic matrix and heat exchangers (both gaseous and liquid) are brought into use. Ferrite devices serve as modulators, and below cutoff waveguides are ideally suited to serve as standard attenuators.

Phase shifting may be accomplished both with dielectric materials and with metallic loading structures. Another approach presently finding favor as a phase shifter is the 3-db hybrid, the output arms of which are adjusted with ganged shorts.

Bolometers, thermistors and crystals of the whisker or varactor type are most commonly used detection devices. Varactor diodes are used in parametric amplifiers, which, when cooled, have noise figures approaching the theoretical limit.

Tunnel diode amplifiers, which do not require cooling to cryogenic temperatures, are becoming even more popular. Lowest noise figures of all, however, are still achieved with MASERS.

Glossary of Symbols

A	(1) wave amplitude; (2) aperture area; (3) aperture linear dimension
a	larger waveguide dimension (parallel to H plane)
B	(1) magnetic flux density; (2) susceptance
b	narrower waveguide dimension (parallel to E plane)
C	(1) capacitance; (2) coupling
c	velocity of light in free-space
D	(1) electric displacement; (2) diameter; (3) directivity
db	decibel(s)
E	electric field intensity
E plane	plane containing E vector
e	$2.718284\ldots$
F	focal distance
f	(1) frequency; (2) f-number (ratio of focal length to aperture)
G	(1) gain; (2) conductance
H	magnetic field intensity
H plane	plane containing H vector
I	current amplitude
i	angle of incidence
J	current density
j	imaginary exponent equaling $\sqrt{-1}$
k	wave number ($2\pi/\lambda$)
L	(1) inductance; (2) distance
l	distance
ln	Napierian logarithm (to base e)
log	Briggsian logarithm (to base 10)
N	integer
n	(1) index of refraction; (2) integer (as subscript or superscript)
P	power
R	(1) radius; (2) radial distance
R_0	characteristic resistance
r	(1) axial ratio; (2) angle of refraction
r.p.	real part of
S	Poynting vector
s	spacing
t	(1) time; (2) thickness

TE	transverse electric wave
TEM	transverse electromagnetic wave
TM	transverse magnetic wave
u	(1) mode constant; (2) $u = \pi x \sin \theta / \lambda$
V	voltage amplitude
VSWR	ratio of maximum to minimum voltage
v	(1) velocity of wave; (2) $v = 2\pi \sin \theta / \lambda$; (3) volts
w	width
X_C	capacitive reactance
X_L	inductive reactance
Y	relative or absolute admittance
Y_0	(1) admittance of free space; (2) characteristic admittance
Z	relative or absolute impedance
Z_L	load impedance
Z_0	(1) impedance of free space; (2) characteristic impedance
Z_{oc}	open-circuited impedance
Z_{sc}	short-circuited impedance
α	(1) geometric angle; (2) attenuation constant
β	(1) geometric angle; (2) $2\pi / \lambda_g$
γ	propagation constant
δ	penetration depth
ϵ	dielectric constant
ζ	normalized impedance
η	(1) power standing wave ratio; (2) efficiency factor; (3) intrinsic impedance
θ	(1) geometric angle; (2) electric angle; (3) phase angle
λ	wavelength
λ_c	cutoff wavelength
λ_g	guide wavelength
μ, μ_r	relative permeability
μ_0	permeability of free space
π	3.141594 ...
ρ	(1) electric charge; (2) reflection coefficient
σ	(1) voltage standing wave ratio; (2) conductivity
τ	transmission coefficient
ϕ	phase
$\Delta\phi$	phase difference
ψ	ray angle
ω	angular velocity

INDEX